" THE FORCES PROPELLING THE WORLD TOWARD MORE
AND GREATER DISASTERS WILL CONTINUE TO OUTWEIGH
BY A WIDE MARGIN THE FORCES PROMOTING A WISE
CHOICE OF ADJUSTMENTS TO HAZARD "

Burton et al (1978) p. 223

Published by M1 PRESS LIMITED
Trent Business Centre
Canal Street
Long Eaton
Nottingham, NG10 4GA
United Kingdom

Telephone (0602) 732485

British Library Cataloguing in Publication Data

Doornkamp, J. C.

The greenhouse effect and rising sea levels in the UK.

I  Climate change - changing sea levels - science, policy,   planning and engineering
II  Doornkamp, J. C.
III M1 PRESS LIMITED

First published 1990

ISBN  1 872792 00 6 The greenhouse effect and rising sea levels in
             the UK. (pbk)

Printed in Great Britain by M1 Press Limited,
Trent Business Centre, Canal Street, Long Eaton, NG10 4GA.
(Tel: (0602) 732485).

Printed on recycled paper.

# ACKNOWLEDGEMENTS

My thanks are due to authors who have contributed so generously to the preparation of this volume. The whole book was stimulated by the excellent series of papers presented at the MAFF (Flood Defence Division) Conference in Loughborough in July of 1989. To these have been added a number of specially commissioned chapters in order to cover aspects which it was not possible to cover during the Conference.

Grateful acknowledgement is made to the owners of copyright material for permission to use that material. Individual copyright holders are identified in the text.


J. C. Doornkamp

# CONTENTS

Page

GLOBAL BACKGROUND

1 The greenhouse effect in its human
context                          J. C. Doornkamp           1

2 The greenhouse effect - the mechanism
for changing sea levels          J. C. Doornkamp           9

3 Global reactions of the oceans and
seas                             R. E. Dugdale            31


UK CONTEXT

4 Sea level rise                  D. T. Pugh               51

5 Effects of sea level rise on the
coastal zone                     I. H. Townend            63

6 Lands at risk from sea level rise
in the UK                        I. R. Whittle            85

7 The greenhouse effect on low-lying
land in Britain                  F. M. Law                95

8 Possible impacts of sea-
level rise - a case study        I. Shennan
from the Tees estuary,           and
Cleveland County                 I. Sproxton             109

# POLICY CONTEXT

9 Policy, planning, and engineering
reactions to sea level rise     *J. C. Doornkamp*     135

10 Department of the Environment
response     *A. J. Apling*     147

Bibliography     151

The greenhouse effect and rising sea
levels a programme of action.     162

# LIST OF FIGURES

FIGURE                                                    Page

1.1 The pattern of reactions to hazardous events            4
1.2 Rising sea level and damage frequency curves            6
2.1 The greenhouse principle                               10
2.2 Global temperature: Departures from the
    1951-79 mean showing general trend                     12
2.3 The relative contributions of individual green-
    house gases to global warming in the 1980s             13
2.4 The trend in carbon dioxide concentrations
    in the atmosphere                                      14
2.5 Long-term temperature changes                          17
2.6 Global warming model proposed by Denness               20
2.7 World average changes in sea level since
    1880                                                   27
2.8 Predictions concerning future changes in
    sea level                                              28
2.9 Reported severe sea floods within the
    North Sea area                                         29
3.1 Global Holocene sea level change due to
    ice cap melting                                        34
3.2 Sea level curves for the British Isles
    during the last 10,000 years                           37
3.3 Present sea level trends in Britain                    43
4.1 Annual sea level records from the four
    most reliable UK sites                                 54
4.2 The global sea level network (GLOSS)                   58
4.3 The UK sea level measuring network oper-
    ated by the Proudman Oceanographic
    Laboratory                                             60
5.1 Estimates of global sea level rise to the
    Year 2050                                              66
5.2 Predicted sea level rise at a) Skegness
    b) Harwich c) Lowestoft d) Southend                    68

5.3 Model predictions of beach erosion during
    a storm for present and increased storm
    surge levels                                          73
5.4 Prediction for the increased distance of
    saline intrusion on the River Trent                   75
5.5 Definition sketch for worked example                  77
5.6 Increase in volume of overtopping per tide            78
5.7 Increase in crest level required for
    a fixed overtopping rate of 0.002 m$^3$/sec           79
5.8 Increase in rock armour weight                        79
6.1 Land close to sea level                               87
6.2 Grade 1-3 agricultural land in England
    and Wales in relation to the
    5m contour                                            89
6.3 Grade 1 agricultural land in England
    and Wales in relation to the
    5m contour                                            90
6.4 Range of predictions for sea level rise at
    an east coast port compared to an
    allowance of 6mm/yr                                   92
8.1 A framework for assessing impacts of
    sea level rise                                       112
8.2 Location map of the Tees estuary                     113
8.3 Wards in eastern England with minimum
    ground altitudes 5m. or lower                        115
8.4 Two scenarios of sea level change                    123
8.5 Sites of special scientific interest
    in the Tees estuary                                  125
8.6 Urban areas in Cleveland                             126
8.7 Industrial areas in Cleveland                        128
8.8 Transport network and areas below 5m OD              129
9.1 Alternative strategies for coping with
    natural hazards                                      137

# LIST OF TABLES

TABLE                                                    Page

1.1 Options available for adjusting to increased
    sea levels                                              7
2.1 Greenhouse gases: Mans' contribution                  15
3.1 Estimated sea level rise by various
    scenarios, 2000 - 2100                                 46
3.2 Sea level changes on continental coast-
    lines due to melting of Greenland and
    Antarctic ice caps                                     47
5.1 Estimated contributions to sea level rise             65
6.1 Sea level trends                                      88
7.1 Distance to coast from 1000 mg/l chloride
    limit                                                  96
7.2 Brackish aquifers arounds the English coasts          97
8.1 Return periods for the Tees and Middles-
    brough docks within the Tees estuary                  121
9.1 Managerial choices in the case of
    large-scale floods in the USA                         139
9.2 Relative costs of actions taken
    at different times                                    142

# LIST OF CONTRIBUTORS

Dr. A. J. Apling — Department of the Environment

Dr. J. C. Doornkamp — Department of Geography, University of Nottingham and Geomorphological Services Limited

Dr. R. E. Dugdale — Department of Geography, University of Nottingham

Mr. F. M. Law — Institute of Hydrology

Dr D. T. Pugh — Institute of Oceanographic Sciences

Dr. I. Shennan — Department of Geography, Universtiy of Durham

Dr. I. Sproxton — Department of Geography, University of Durham

Mr. I. H. Townend — Sir William Halcrow & Partners

Mr. I. R. Whittle — National Rivers Authority

# THE GREENHOUSE EFFECT IN ITS

# HUMAN CONTEXT

## J. C. DOORNKAMP

This book is about the greenhouse effect and rising sea levels with special reference to the UK coastline. The only reason why there is an interest in this subject is that there is concern about the impact that such a rise in sea level may have on the human occupance of the coastline. In particular there is concern about the need for, and the appropriate nature of, advanced planning to cope with the changes that will take place.

The immediate human reaction to such a problem is usually a defensive one. "Throw up the barriers" will be a common response, though probably not until damaging effects from a rising sea level start to be felt. Research elsewhere has shown (Burton et al 1978) that in the case of natural hazards of which people have little or no personal experience the majority of inhabitants will either deny that there is a risk or will assert that they do not regard it as a problem for themselves or their neighbours. The greenhouse effect-rising sea levels scenario is therefore a human as well as a physical problem, and must be dealt with in that light. This point is taken up again in Chapter 9.

This book presents a synthesis of the greenhouse effect, the global warming which accompanies it, and the likely consequential sea level reactions that may be expected. However, as the opening paragraphs to this chapter suggest, rising sea levels are only a hazard in so far as they have a human impact. There is a social dimension to this situation which needs to be explored and which provides the context of any likely reactions to any sea level changes that may occur.

*Greenhouse effect and rising UK sea levels*

This chapter, therefore, looks at the human context of natural hazards and describes the more important aspects which have been identified by hazard studies in the past. Such studies include those of Burton, Kates and Snead (1969), White and Haas (1975), and others, who have been much concerned with the human ecology of natural hazards, especially flooding. This is done in order to indicate the nature of the reactions that may be expected in this case.

## The concept of tolerance

Whenever a dynamic natural event, such as a flood, occurs there is often a point or threshold beyond which human tolerance is at an end and a reaction takes place which is designed to counter that event. This reaction may be in the form of a movement of people away from the affected sites or it may be manifest as an attempt to control (ie. engineer) the site.

"Tolerance" in this context is a function of the ability of the community, in terms of its social organisation and its engineering abilities, to cope with such events. Vulnerability is therefore a function of the ability to cope as well as the level of the hazard itself.

## Perception

The ability to cope in the case of most developed industrial societies is not usually called into question. What is much more likely to bring about a "natural disaster" is a failure to perceive the nature and the magnitude of extreme events as they really will be. Basic decisions (eg. about coast protection works) are made on the basis of past experience in the expectation that (at least for the most part) the actions taken are sufficient to cope with extreme events. This is represented by the stippled zone in Figure 1.1. If the basic nature of the event (eg. sea level or the height attained by sea storms) changes then the earlier controls brought in to cope with the event may themselves be inadequate and the now accepted tolerance level is exceeded.

At this point further actions are determined by the perception of the managers involved. One of three alternatives are likely. There may be a perception that extreme events are happening which have a very long recurrence interval (eg. once in every 200 years, or longer). In which case no further action will be taken. Alternatively it may be decided that such events could occur again on a shorter time-scale and a second phase of controls are brought in to reduce further damage and to create yet another tolerance level that is then perceived to be adequate. A third possibility is that the event itself is on an upward trend, historical records and back-calculated recurrence intervals are irrelevant, and the managers concerned, realising this, take innovative actions to cope. These actions may include the defensive stand referred to at the beginning of this chapter, or it may involve a retreat away from the affected sites.

**Defining the hazard**

The standard way of defining a natural hazard is in terms of its:

magnitude, extent, frequency and duration.

In practice magnitude and frequency, and to some extent duration, are statistical concepts that may be defined in terms of different extents of influence. The most familiar use of these concepts is in terms of river flooding. Such statistics are based on historical records and their predictive value lies in the future behaving like the past. If the future takes on a different manner of behaviour such statistics will not provide a realistic basis for assessing future behaviour (see Chapter 4).

4

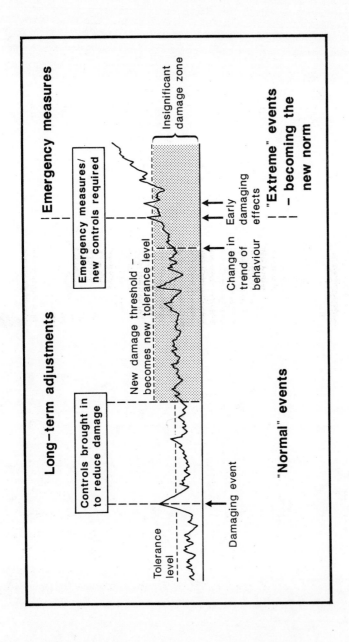

FIGURE 1.1 THE PATTERN OF REACTIONS TO HAZARDOUS EVENTS
(Loosely based on Hewitt and Burton, 1971)

## Defining the impact

It is difficult to define a hazard in human terms. A hazard takes on a cost when it makes contact with something of "value" to people. This may take the form of a life, limb or property. Indeed the usual basis for defining the impact of a natural hazard is in terms of economic loss and loss of life.

Cost-benefit economics can only be broadly applied at this time in anticipation of future land-use/rising sea level scenarios. Some early attempts at this type of analysis was carried out by Eckstein (1958) and by Sewell (1964) in relation to river flooding. A study by Sewell (1965) of flooding in the Fraser River Basin provides the basis for Figure 1.2 which illustrates the potential relationships that may be realised between rising sea levels, increased storminess and the costs of damage. This can only be taken as a model and would require calibration in individual circumstances.

## Strategy in relation to the greenhouse effect and rising sea levels

The task of coastal zone hazard management is one of reducing the potential for loss in either terms. Such a task is similar to that of managers concerned with earthquake or flood prone areas in that a theoretical range of options are available for coping with, or adjusting to, the potential problems of an increased sea level (Table 1.1).

It is clear from an analysis of other natural hazards and their impact that the "best" strategies for adjustment come from an integrated approach which combines the best that both technology and human planning and behaviour can provide. However, to do so requires an agreed set of objectives. If the objectives are not defined first then it is impossible to decide on how to achieve them, and impossible to recognise when they have been achieved.

6

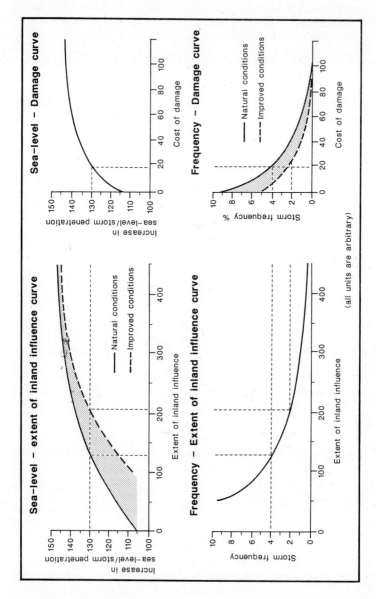

**FIGURE 1.2 RISING SEA LEVEL AND DAMAGE FREQUENCY CURVES**
(Modification of flood discharge curves in Sewell, 1965)

## TABLE 1.1

## OPTIONS AVAILABLE FOR ADJUSTING TO INCREASED SEA LEVELS

### A. DEALING WITH THE HAZARD

OPTION

| | |
|---|---|
| Prevent the rise in sea level | Option not available except by preventing the greenhouse effect |
| Modify the hazard | Coast protection by all available means including engineering works |
| Modify the loss potential | Land use changes, planning controls, emergency preparedness |

### B. DEALING WITH ANY LOSSES

| | |
|---|---|
| Spread the losses | Public relief, subsidised insurance |
| Plan for losses | Insurance and reserve funds |
| Bear the losses | Individual loss bearing |

**Based on: Sewell (1965); and Burton, Kates and White (1968)**

*Greenhouse effect and rising UK sea levels*

8

It is not difficult to convert the general model shown in Figure 1.1 into a specific model with reference to the greenhouse effect and the potential for rising sea levels. The general model helps to show that different coastal management units, because they have been subject to different controls in the past, will currently possess different damage thresholds. This must mean that future experiences of changing sea levels may well be different from place to place around the UK coastline.

What each "coastal manager" has to decide is what the future holds with respect to rising sea levels not only in general but also in relation to the section of coast that is under their care. If the decision is made to do something then in practice (following Hewitt and Burton, 1971) four basic questions have to be answered:

1. Is there a **technically feasible** solution ?
2. Is the solution **economically justified** ?
3. Is the solution **socially acceptable** ?
4. Is the solution **environmentally sound** (not least in terms of consequential coastal dynamics) ?

This book has been compiled in order to provide some help to those who are faced with these responsibilities.

# THE GREENHOUSE EFFECT

# - THE MECHANISM FOR CHANGING SEA LEVELS

## J. C. DOORNKAMP

There is now a general presumption that mankind has induced a period of global warming, due to the so called "greenhouse effect", and that one of the consequences of this will be a global rise in sea level. Most of this book concentrates on the rising sea level scenario. This chapter, however, provides a summary account of the greenhouse effect, its causes, and the anticipated nature of any climatic changes which will be associated with it. Much fuller accounts will be found in some of the bibliographic references, but it is necessary to focus here on the main issues as these form the background to the whole of the rest of this book.

### The Greenhouse Effect

The analogy drawn between a greenhouse and its protective layer of glass, and the earth with its protective layer of "greenhouse gasses" is a very effective one (Fig 2.1). They both cause heat to be retained (i.e. within the greenhouse and the earth respectively.)

The greenhouse gasses include $CO_2$, methane, CFCs (chlorofluorocarbons), nitrous oxide and ozone, and their presence as a layer around the globe has enabled the world to have a temperature some 30°C higher than would otherwise be the case. The presence of this layer has allowed life, as we know it, to develop and be maintained.

So what has changed? In brief, an increase in global temperatures

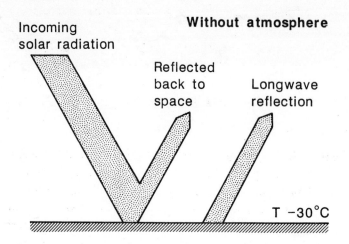

Incoming
solar radiation

**Without atmosphere**

Reflected
back to
space

Longwave
reflection

T −30°C

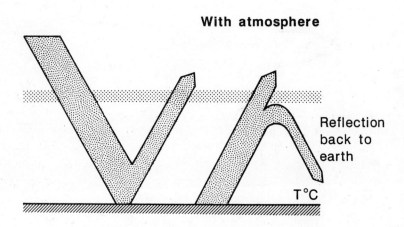

**With atmosphere**

Reflection
back to
earth

T°C

**FIGURE 2.1  THE GREENHOUSE PRINCIPLE**

*The mechanism for changing sea levels*

has been detected (Fig 2.2) which appears to many scientists to be greater than that which could be expected from natural trends alone. The cause for this increase has been attributed very largely to the inputs of greenhouse gasses into the atmosphere by human activity (e.g. coal burning to produce $CO_2$), thereby increasing their concentration (see Table 2.1) and bringing about an increase in the amount of heat reflected back towards the earth.

The relative contributions of each of the greenhouse gases to global warming in the 1980s is shown in Figure 2.3. The recent increase in $CO_2$ concentrations in the atmosphere (parts per million by volume) is shown in Figure 2.4.

## The Record of Climatic Change

It is more or less undisputed that there has been a global-mean temperature rise of 0.5°C over the past 100 years. There have been considerable annual and seasonal variations around this trend, including a tendency for temperatures to fall during the 20 years or so after the mid-1940s, but the long-term records tend to confirm this view.

The data in Figure 2.2 show world-wide averaged temperatures compared with the mean for the period 1951-79, and show that since 1937 there has been an increasing tendency for particular years to exceed that mean, and a continual upward trend through the whole data set since 1860. It is this underlying trend which causes so much concern, especially when it is seen to fit climatic models that predict even greater increases in the future (see below).

On a longer time scale comparisons can be made with changes in temperature since the Ice Age. At that time, 10,000-20,000 years ago, the earth was only 5°C colder than average temperatures today. The adjustment from those temperatures has taken about 10,000 years to

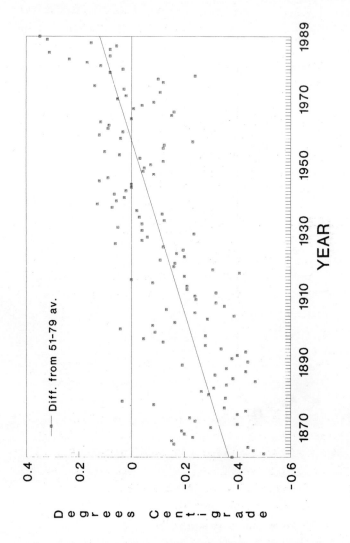

FIGURE 2.2 GLOBAL TEMPERATURE: DEPARTURES FROM THE 1951-79 MEAN SHOWING GENERAL TREND (data from Gribbin and Kelly, 1989)

*The mechanism for changing sea levels*

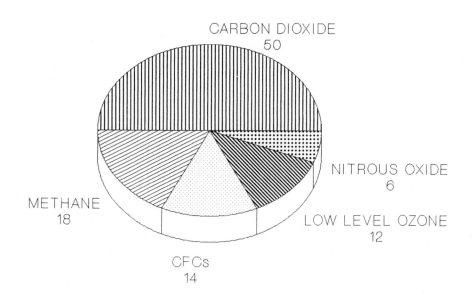

CARBON DIOXIDE
50

NITROUS OXIDE
6

METHANE
18

LOW LEVEL OZONE
12

CFCs
14

**FIGURE 2.3 THE RELATIVE CONTRIBUTIONS OF
INDIVIDUAL GREENHOUSE GASES
TO GLOBAL WARMING IN THE 1980s**
(data from Natural Environment
Research Council, 1989)

*Greenhouse effect and rising UK sea levels*

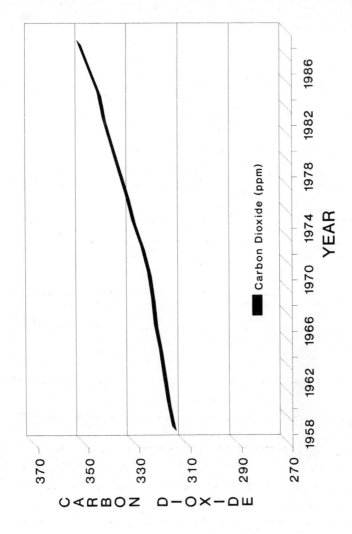

FIGURE 2.4 THE TREND IN CARBON DIOXIDE CONCENTRATIONS IN THE
ATMOSPHERE   (data from Gribbin and Kelly, 1989)

*The mechanism for changing sea levels*

## TABLE 2.1

## GREENHOUSE GASES: MAN'S CONTRIBUTION

$CO_2$: produced by the burning of coal, gas, oil and wood.

-24% increase in atmospheric concentrations over the past 150 years, and about 0.5% per annum for the past 20 years.

CFCs: produced through the use of some types of aerosols, and found in some good trays, domestic freezers and refrigerators, commercial refrigeration systems, and most air - conditioning systems.

- concentrations have increased at a rate of about 5% per annum over the past 10 years. Did not occur in the atmosphere prior to 1950.

methane: produced from paddy fields and by animals (especially bovines)

-levels have risen at a rate of 1% per annum over the past 10 years.

nitrous oxide: produced by nitrogen fertilizers and is also a by-product of the combustion process.

- concentrations have increased at a rate of 0.25% per annum over the past decade.

ozone: produced by the action of sunlight on nitrogen oxides, hydrocarbons and carbon monoxide (e.g. vehicle exhaust emissions)

- ozone levels in the troposphere (below and within the greenhouse gases layer) may have doubled over the past century.

*Greenhouse effect and rising UK sea levels*

be achieved (i.e. an average rate of warming of 0.5°C every **1000 years**. This observation places the present rate of temperature increase ( 0.5°C in **100 years**) in an interesting, and some would say alarming, context.

Over an even longer time scale (Fig. 2.5) equivalent high temperatures to those of today were present some 120,000 to 130,000 years ago.

Such comparisons, of course, are dangerous for present rates of change upwards may be followed, on a longer time-scale by almost equal changes downwards and the average may then fit, once again, to the post-Pleistocene trends. Historical comparisons are therefore better made with fluctuations over equivalent periods of time (i.e. over 100-150 year periods).

There are further complications in that changes have taken place, and are taking place, at different rates in different parts of the world. It is relevant to note, however, that around 18,000 years B.P. sea levels were some 110-120 m. lower around the world. Since then sea level rise has averaged about 8 mm/annum, and at one stage (about 5000 BP) stood some 2-4 m. above present levels before falling to the present-day levels to which we have adjusted many of our activities. It is notable that these higher sea levels coincided with temperatures some 0.5-1.0°C higher than present. However, isostatic adjustments through crustal movements have also taken place in that time (see Chapter 3). Nevertheless, such observation do encourage some authors (e.g. Idso 1988) to feel that more of the present trend is due to natural post "Little Ice Age" responses than to the effects of green-house gases. This "Little Ice Age" lasted from about 1400-1700 AD. However, others comment that, as compared with similar events, this one is appreciably shorter, possibly due to the intervention of man (Mitchell, 1972, 1977).

It should be noted that any significant rise in temperature will be associated with other changes in climate. In particular there is likely

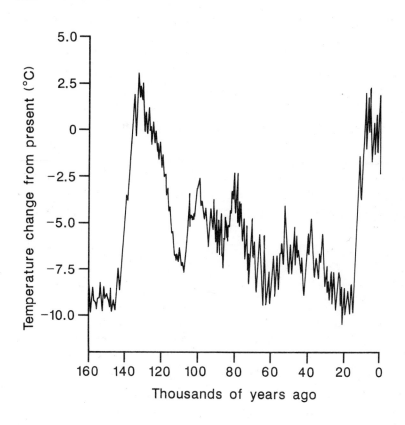

**FIGURE 2.5 LONG-TERM TEMPERATURE
CHANGES**

*Greenhouse effect and rising UK sea levels*

to be an increase in summer dryness in the middle latitudes, increased rainfall in the late winter, and probably an increase in storminess (see below).

## Predictions of future temperature change

Any prediction of future temperature changes must be based on:
- recent (historical) trends
- awareness of controlling parameters (and how they are likely to change)
- the model(s) used to make the prediction.

One way of testing a model is to compare what has happened in the recent past with predictions made for that time from earlier data. This helps to calibrate the model and tests its sensitivity. Whether or not it can then be used accurately to predict future trends (and specific values) will depend on the underlying assumptions of the model remaining true. In particular, the parameters that control global warming (i.e. greenhouse gases) must achieve their predicted concentrations if the model(s) are to remain valid. Whether or not this is achieved cannot be known until after the event.

All models, which attempt to predict future temperature conditions, therefore, are open to criticism (even scepticism in some cases). Even more uncertain is any prediction of rising sea levels. Quite simply this is because the predicted temperature values are needed before the sea level values can be predicted. Nevertheless, bearing these caveats in mind it is relevant to note that scientists do not seriously doubt that the "greenhouse effect" is taking place, though there are differing predictions about future climatic conditions. The purpose of the rest of this chapter is to review some of the climatic models that have been proposed and to note the temperature changes that have been predicted.

*The mechanism for changing sea levels*

## A Linear Model

A model for predicting temperature change was proposed by Dennes in 1984 and re-presented by him in 1989 (see Hall and Doornkamp, 1989). This is a linear model which predicts natural changes in temperature according to the relationship:

$$G(t) = \sum_{n=N(T)}^{\infty} A(T).\ a^n.\ \sin\left\{b^{1-n}.\ \pi(\frac{t}{T})\right\}$$

which is zero-registered at time To and in which G(t) is a time-based climate index.

Figure 2.6 compares actual northern hemisphere temperatures (Fig. 2.6a) during the period 1880-1980 as differences from the mean for 1980 with natural temperatures predicted according to the above model (Fig. 2.6b). By subtracting the predicted from the actual values the a-b curve in Figure 2.6c is obtained, whose 15-year running mean can be smoothed to indicate a rising trend that measures the deviation of the actual from the predicted. This line is identified as the rise in temperature due to the greenhouse effect.

The combination of the greenhouse component and the natural component in this model comes close to describing observed historical changes in temperature. It "fits" the 1.5°C rise experienced between 1830 and 1860, as well as more recent temperature fluctuations. If allowed to run into the future the model forecasts a global temperature rise of almost 1°C during the next decade.

## Global Climatic Models (GCMs)

Such models attempt to include a spatial component in their prediction by concentrating on global circulation patterns. They include data not only on temperature but also on wind and storm tracks (and their seasonal variations). However, they are too gener-

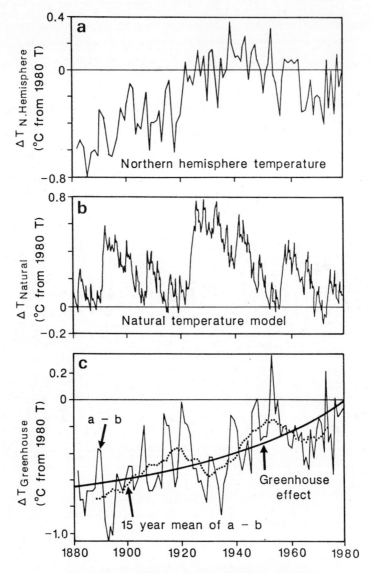

**FIGURE 2.6 GLOBAL WARMING MODEL
PROPOSED BY DENNESS**
(from Hall and Doornkamp, 1989)

*The mechanism for changing sea levels*

alized to include regional patterns of precipitation, currents and tides (Hansen et al; 1986, 1988).

GCMs (eg. that proposed by Hansen et al; 1986, 1988) are usually based on a division of the world into grid cells (typically 5 degrees of latitude by 7 degrees of longitude) for each of which vertical layers (usually nine or more) are identified through the ocean layers or the ground, and the atmosphere. Circulation effects are defined by exchanges between the cells, and vertical effects by exchanges between the layers. Basic laws of physics (i.e. Newton's second law of motion, the first law of thermodynamics, the ideal gas law and the continuity equation) are used to calculate the transfer of mass, energy and momentum from one grid cell to another (i.e. representing circulation effects). Similar calculations allow the vertical inter-layer effects within each cell to be simulated.

It has been difficult to include the role of sea ice in such models. Sea ice tends to be represented as a thermodynamic slab, with little account taken of ice movement and this is particularly important in relation to the growth and decay of the Antarctic ice pack (Cattle, 1989).

As $CO_2$ concentrations are increased in the GCM it is found that time-averaged circulation patterns change (eg. the circulation patterns over the northern hemisphere in January). Such changes imply that the weather patterns will change and this will include changes in storminess, with a general prediction that in the mid-latitudes storminess will increase.

Such models, once again, can be tested on historical data and used to predict future trends. One advantage of GCMs over linear models is that they allow global variations to be identified and thereby add a spatial dimension not directly available from the linear model.

### Discussion of the Models

Any prediction is only as good as the model (and original data) from which it is derived. By definition all models try to emulate reality, they are not reality themselves. Furthermore, the assumptions used in the establishment of a model may change as time passes, and thereby render that model less useful.

The danger is that lay-members of the community will accept the results of model predictions while forgetting the original "ifs" and "buts" attached to the model itself.

What has to be remembered in the case of the models discussed above is that they have been calibrated against historical data. Such data belong to a period whose environmental conditions may not be replicated in the future. In which case the model may fail to make precise predictions.

Lamb (1972) also cautions that greenhouse warming has to be balanced against the possibility of cooling arising from the natural changes that are taking place. In addition, the feedback effects resulting from the increase in greenhouse gases (eg. consequential re-actions operating through the oceans and atmospheric water vapour) may greatly affect the accuracy of predictions.

To the extent that a model is based on physical laws (as is the GCM described above) its predictive accuracy will depend on set assumptions about such things as the additional inputs of greenhouse gases which are likely to occur. These are themselves subject to estimations. For example, in many GCMs the measure used is the combined radiative effect of all greenhouse gases expressed as a $CO_2$ equivalent, and calculations are then based on a doubling of this $CO_2$ equivalent.

The $CO_2$ concentrations of 280 ppmv (in the mid-18th century pre-industrial revolution world) are expected to rise to 560 ppmv by the year 2030. Today levels stand at about 350 ppmv, so we are 25% of the way there (Table 2.1).

Should such a doubling in $CO_2$ equivalent take place, however, then the predictions are for a rise of somewhere between 1.5°C and 4.5°C in the global-mean surface air temperatures by the year 2030, as compared with the values that would occur without such an increase in $CO_2$ equivalents.

The range 1.5-4.5°C is huge, in climatic change terms; and the consequences (in terms of the potential for sea level rise for instance) are very different at the two ends of this range.

The oceans themselves, of course, play a significant part in the whole story as they have the ability to absorb some of this rise in temperature. Such absorption has the effect of lengthening the time it takes to reach an ultimate equilibrium state, if indeed such a state can ever be achieved. In the meantime the effect of the oceans will be to reduce the estimated rise in temperature to between 0.5°C and 2.5°C.

A distinction is made in the running of these models between an **equilibrium response** (the ultimate change in the climate) and the **transient response** (the temporary states that occur in the climate on the progression towards an ultimate state).

In reality there may never be an ultimate state. It is possible to predict through GCMs what conditions may be like in 50 years time, but even then changes will continue to take place.

A second important concept is that of a time-lag between the initiation of a change and the response which it generates. For example, if all emission and production of greenhouse gases were to cease today there would continue to be a climatic response as climate adjusted to the greenhouse gases already released. Part of this is because of the lag time within ocean systems to respond to global

*Greenhouse effect and rising UK sea levels*

warming. This factor is further complicated by the considerable variations that exist from one part of the globe to another.

A complication in all such modelling is that there are feedback mechanisms in operation. For example, the types of climatic change under discussion have an effect on: water vapour content of the atmosphere, cloud/ radiation/ temperature interactions, sea ice, snow and land ice. Changes in any of these may either amplify or reduce certain affects. It has been estimated that in the absence of such feedback effects if a doubling of carbon dioxide concentrations led to an increase of 1.2°C in global mean surface temperature then the increase in water vapour content that would accompany this would add a further 0.5°C to this effect, and the decrease in snow and ice cover would further increase global warming by a similar amount (Cattle, 1989). Likewise the estimation of the influence of global warming on cloudiness is open to considerable debate, and yet the amounts of cloud present in the atmosphere will have a significant bearing on the actual temperatures achieved.

It is important to remember that longer-term studies suggest that our present inter-glacial will come to an end. The first climax of the next glacial period will occur sometime between 3000 and 7000 years from now (Berger, 1980). Hence, in general terms and over a long enough time period the background "natural" tendency is towards global cooling.

This overall tendency does NOT preclude the possibility of several centuries of global warming due to the emission of greenhouse gases as a result of human activity.

One large uncertainty in all of this is the future role of mankind. Changes in the emission of greenhouse gases may take place to the point where the shorter term predictions will be proved wrong. A world-wide environmental-political lobby may lead to such changes in our way of life that the upward trend in global temperatures may

*The mechanism for changing sea levels*

be arrested. Forest regeneration (especially in the tropics) may reduce atmospheric levels of $CO_2$. Changes that lead away from the use of fossil fuels may reduce $CO_2$ emissions. On the other hand the continued industrialisation of some countries (perhaps especially China with its large reserves of coal) will lead to an even greater rate of $CO_2$ emissions than has been predicted. The issues are complex and have been discussed elsewhere (see Hall and Doornkamp, 1989).

The paradox is that the least determinable factor in climatic prediction is the role to be played by mankind - the very factor that is in our own (collective) hands.

### Predicted Temperature Increases

As described above the best estimates of a global-mean surface air temperature rise by the year 2030 is 0.5 - 2.5°C. There is an assumption that the true figure will be in the range 1.0-2.0°C, giving the highest global temperature for about 120,000 years (Fig. 2.5). It is interesting to note that these recent estimates are not very different from those given by Plass in 1949 who recognised the potential impact of the emission of $CO_2$ and anticipated a further temperature rise of 2.6°C by the turn of the century.

It cannot be assumed, however, that such a temperature rise will be uniformly distributed around the globe. GCMs by definition deal with variations and patterns around the world, and their seasonal variations. Figure 2.5 shows one prediction, linked to an effective doubling of $CO_2$ equivalents, for the winter and summer months. The greater increases predicted for the polar latitudes are, of course, most significant in terms of the melting of ice and the consequent effect on rising sea levels. However, the observed amounts of warming to date in the higher latitudes do not appear to be as great as those that are predicted by running most GCMs through the appropriate time periods.

## Predicted changes in precipitation

Most GCMs predict an average increase in precipitation world-wide of about 10%. Once again such a change will not be equally distributed across the world. High latitudes are expected to see the greatest increases, with the related increases in run-off that this will generate. Middle latitudes are also likely to see something of an increase in precipitation, but there is a consensus emerging that there will also be a reduction in soil moisture over the mid-latitude continents in the summer. This may be less likely over maritime Britain.

## Predicted changes in sea level

Later chapters deal with the prediction of changes in sea level in some detail. Chapter 3 reviews changes since the Holocene and other chapters consider the immediate future. Two strands of these considerations need to be identified here. The first concerns recorded changes in mean sea level over the immediate past, and the second cocerns the predictions that have been made for the immediate future.

The nature of changes in world average sea levels since 1880 are shown in Figure 2.7. In the first part of this period (1880 - 1940) levels were below their 1880 position. Since 1941 they have continued to rise. As far as the prediction of changes in the near-future are concerned (Fig. 2.8) there are extremes in the current predictions, but all indicate that there is a general expectation for levels to continue to rise.

## Predicted changes in storminess

Amongst coastal engineers there is as great a concern about the predicted increase in storm events as there is about average sea levels.

*The mechanism for changing sea levels*

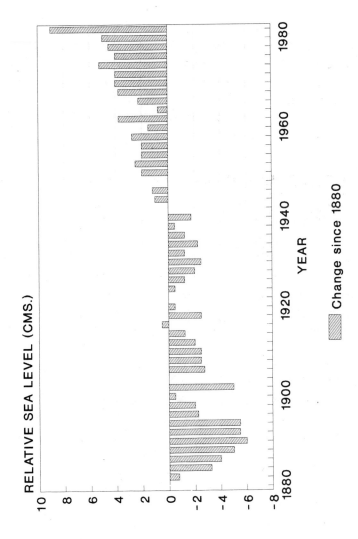

RELATIVE SEA LEVEL (CMS.)

YEAR

Change since 1880

FIGURE 2.7 WORLD AVERAGE CHANGES IN SEA LEVEL SINCE 1880

*Greenhouse effect and rising UK sea levels*

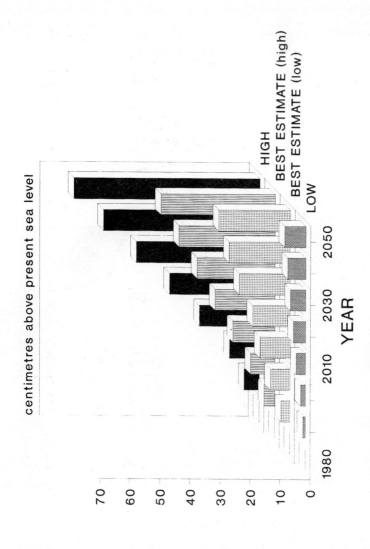

**FIGURE 2.8 PREDICTIONS CONCERNING FUTURE CHANGES IN SEA LEVEL**
(After Warrick et al, 1989)

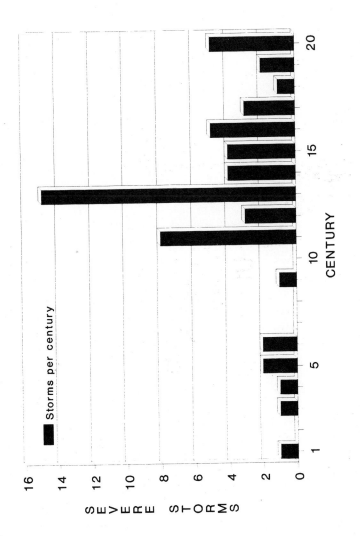

**FIGURE 2.9 REPORTED SEVERE SEA FLOODS WITHIN THE NORTH SEA AREA**

(after Lamb, 1982)

*Greenhouse effect and rising UK sea levels*

The main reason is that a storm on top of a higher sea level will pose a greater threat and possibly cause more damage than is currently the case. Predictions that storminess will increase (especially perhaps in the mid-latitudes) are likely to cause a re-assessment of the effectiveness of sea defences (see Chapter 5).

In an analysis of reported severe sea floods within the North Sea (Fig. 2.9) Lamb (1982) shows that storm floods reached a maxima in the eleventh and thirteenth centuries AD, with more severe floods in, and soon after, late Roman times and again in the twentieth century than at other periods. The common factor in each case has been (i) raised sea levels after long periods of warm climate and glacial melting, and (ii) a cooling Arctic producing stronger thermal gradients between latitudes 50 and 65°N. This provides an historical parallel with today's situation.

## Conclusion

Despite the caveats and discrepancies between prediction and reality which appear to exist in the prediction of climatic change, it is clear that the consensus view is that global warming is a reality. The importance of this becomes apparent when it is realised that the "natural" climate currently has a preferred tendency to cooling. The observed global warming will not only be apparent as a temperature change, it will also involve changes in rainfall, runoff, soil-moisture, and storminess. This latter on top of higher sea levels is likely to be of greatest significance in the whole saga of consequential effects along the UK coastline.

This aspect is taken up in greater detail in the subsequent chapters in this book. The discussions in these chapters are all set against the greenhouse effect as the driving mechanism for change within the life-span of existing engineering structures, buildings, land uses and a variety of economic investments.

# 3

# GLOBAL REACTIONS OF THE OCEANS

# AND SEAS

## R. E. DUGDALE

That sea level has changed with respect to time has been established for many years. Until recently the majority of academic endeavour has been directed towards the elucidation and publication of regional sea level curves for many parts of the world covering all or part of the period of sea level recovery since the last glacial maximum (sea level minimum) some 18,000 years ago.

Over the last two decades it has become increasingly evident that there is also a significant spatial component of sea level change. Somewhat less effort has been applied to the equally important question of the causes and mechanisms of sea level change - a question which must be increasingly addressed if models and predictions of future sea level change are to be confidently accepted.

Over the last decade considerable emphasis has been placed on the human factor both in terms of causes and responses to sea level change. Global warming associated with the accumulation of greenhouse gases in the atmosphere is likely to be the primary forcing factor of sea level change over the next few centuries. Such changes are likely to be of sufficient magnitude that they must occupy a central position in coastal management decision-making and strategies in terms of both planning and protection. If sensible responses are to be made to anticipated sea level change then strategies need to be considered and adopted both at local and national levels (see Chapter 9). This chapter reviews the evidence for past, present and future sea level variations, with emphasis on the latter, and assesses some of the major implications for planners, managers, engineers and occupants of low lying coastal areas.

## Past sea level changes

From a management point of view knowledge of past sea level changes at a particular location can be significant if the geomorphic and sedimentary responses to those changes are established and understood. Stability or instability of modern coastal environments and likely consequences of future sea level change can then be assessed, where relevant, in the light of past sensitivities and responses within the coastal system. Of some importance in this context is the length of time for which sea level has been relatively stable at any location and, therefore, the period available for adjustments between processes and landforms. This consideration is particularly pertinent in the context of features of the coastal system which require relatively long periods of time for adjustment, for example cliffline stability.

The history of sea level change at any one locality will be determined by one or more of the complex components which determine relative movements of sea level. On the global scale the major component of past sea level change is termed *eustatic* and is associated with the movement of water from the oceanic to the terrestrial environment and vice-versa associated with the growth and decay of large continental ice sheets.

The changing distribution of mass on the earth's surface associated with this migration of water also created other components of sea level change which were of both global and local significance. The removal and subsequent addition of mass from the world's oceanic basins and continental shelves during successive periods of glaciation and deglaciation resulted in hydro-isostatic adjustments in the earth's crust. Unloading during periods of glaciation due to lower sea levels caused positive relative movements of oceanic and shelf areas. Loading following deglaciation and sea level rise resulted in negative relative movements.

Land areas which sustained ice caps were subject to glacio-isostatic components of relative movement. During glacial periods these areas were depressed relative to sea level but rebounded to approximately former levels once the ice load had been removed. Maximum depression and subsequent recovery is associated with the central areas of former ice sheets where ice thicknesses were at a maximum. There is growing evidence that the areas immediately surrounding the ice sheets sustained a positive fore-bulge at the time of glaciation related to transfer of materials within the earth's crust associated with the ice loading. Once the ice sheet melted crustal material returned to the area of glacio-isostatic depression and the fore-bulge collapsed. Clearly any area which was either in close proximity to, or, was within former areas of glaciation will have experienced a complex sea level history which will be a function of the varying rates of both eustatic and isostatic components through time.

The changing distribution of mass over the surface of the globe must have resulted in changes in geoid configuration, the equipotential surface of the earth (Morner, 1976). Although the mechanisms and, therefore, time scales of such changes have not been reliably established they must seriously condition interpretation of past sea level movements in that any published sea level curve may only be considered to be of local, or at best, regional application.

A theoretical study by Clark et al (1978) develops the implications of geoid changes due to changing ice and water loads on a spherical visco-elastic Earth in terms of non-uniform sea level rise in different parts of the world's oceans during the last 18,000 years. Results from the study (Fig. 3.1) suggest that six zones can be recognised within the world's oceans which have specific forms of relative sea level curves. In four of the zones a period of relative fall of sea level or emergence is predicted. In the remaining two zones submergence has been dominant throughout the time interval.

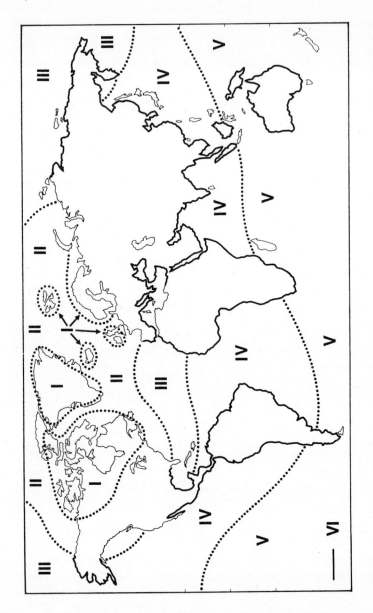

FIGURE 3.1 GLOBAL HOLOCENE SEA LEVEL CHANGE DUE TO ICE CAP MELTING

(Map above: Behaviour graphs below)

*Global reactions of oceans and seas*

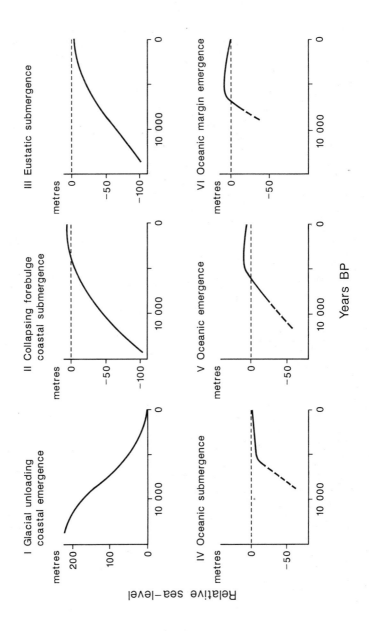

Greenhouse effect and rising UK sea levels

An excellent review of Holocene (last 10,000 years) global sea level change scenarios is given by Kidson (1982), which covers the period of well-documented sea level recovery since the last period of major global glaciation. The same review also includes a discussion of errors associated with datums, dating and sea level indicators which often lead to differences of interpretation of the evidence of sea level change at any particular site.

One major issue which arises from this review which is pertinent to coastal planning is the date of attainment of present sea level. It is now clear that present sea level was not reached synchronously around the world and that the actual date of attainment at any particular locality will depend on the tectonic setting and possible geoid migrations (see the next section of this chapter).

Many published curves suggest relatively static sea levels for the last 4000 years. However, disagreement still exists even within relatively small areas. In many areas of the world, particularly in Australia, there is evidence of sea level a little higher than present in the relatively recent past. It is still not clear if this high stand represents a global eustatic component or a more local tectonic or geoidal effect.

An overview of sea level changes in England and Wales during the Flandrian is given by Shennan(1983). Review papers of sea level history are also available for different parts of the British coast. Sea level curves covering much of the British Isles are shown in Figure 3.2. It should be noted that some of these curves were originally published, in what is now the generally accepted form, with significant error bands related to uncertainties in height and date determinations. The liberty of drawing actual curves has been taken in the interest of clarity for this review paper but the reader is strongly recommended to refer to original publications if detailed information about particular areas is required.

*Global reactions of oceans and seas*

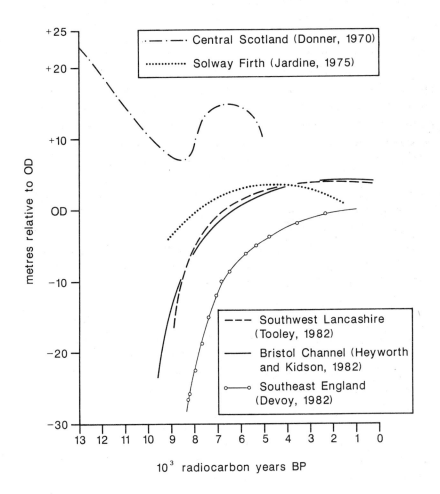

**FIGURE 3.2 SEA LEVEL CURVES FOR THE
BRITISH ISLES DURING THE LAST 10,000 YEARS**

38

The southeast of England is covered in a rigorous review by Devoy (1982) who presents evidence of sea level rising from -30 m OD at about 9300 BP. A period of stillstand or distinct reduction in the rate of sea level rise appears to have occurred between about 4500 and 3000 BP with a possible highstand at +0.5 m OD around 1700 BP. The southwest of England, the Channel Islands and Wales are covered by Heyworth and Kidson (1982). Here sea level at 9000 BP is slightly more than 30 m below present sea level which compares well with the figure from the southeast. A significant slowing in the rate of rise occurred about 6000 BP when sea level was still some 6 m below present and there is no evidence of any highstands of sea level.

Northern England is covered by Tooley (1982). Two time-depth graphs are presented for southwest Lancashire and Morecambe Bay. Both suggest sea level was close to -15 m OD at 9000 BP. A very rapid rise in level occurred between 8000 and 7600 BP which began to slow significantly about 6000 BP. Since this time sea level has remained relatively constant. Shennan(1987) gives a comprehensive account of curves from the North Sea region.

The sea level history of Scotland is much more complex since the area sustained a large ice cap much later than England and still has a positive glacio-isostatic component of readjustment as a consequence of the removal of crustal loading following the final melting of the ice some 10000 years ago.

A comprehensive review is contained in Jardine (1982). At the maximum of the last glacial some 18,000 years ago sea level in Scotland probably stood around -60 m OD. However, shorelines dating from the period around 13,000 years ago now stand at +50 m OD on the east coast and +40 m OD in the west. The curves which have been published for the period from 10,000 BP represent the delicate and continually changing balance between glacio-isostatic and eustatic components. All these curves, except for those from the Solway Firth, show evidence of a relative fall in sea level between about 10,000 and 8,500BP when glacio-isostatic effects associated with the final removal of the ice burden were greater than the eustatic component. However, after about 8,500 BP the eustatic rise in sea level became dominant and there was a relative rise in sea level equivalent to the Holocene transgression elsewhere in the British Isles. Coastline features associated with this transgression are known as the Main Postglacial Shoreline which has been subsequently uplifted following the subsequent re-establishment, and continuation, of glacio-isostatic dominance as the eustatic effect declined through time. This fall in sea level began around 6000 BP in the Forth Valley but not until after 5000 BP in the Solway area. This apparent time shift in the regression is related to the distance from the centre of uplift.

**Present sea level variations**

Present variations of sea level, both spatially and on relatively short timescales, will now be reviewed since knowledge, both in terms of understanding and prediction, of such variations is an essential element in present coastal management. Also since such variations will persist into the future their effects must be incorporated into forward models of longer term sea level change. Spatially the ocean surface is highly uneven with a relief relative to the geoid, the global reference datum for height determination, of as much as 180 m (-105 and +75 m). These variations were termed by Morner (1979) the geodetic sea level and are related to changes in the earth's gravity field which in turn is essentially related to anomalies in the distribution of mass. Changes in height of the order of metres to tens of metres occur over distances of thousands of kilometres. Decimetre changes may occur over distances of 30 km. It is quite likely that the geoid configuration changes with time but because of the relatively large spatial and temporal extents of such changes they may have little significance in terms of design criteria for coastal engineering projects at any particular location. However, any future sea level change scenarios at global and, to a lesser extent, at local levels will have to take account of the redistribution of mass and, therefore, potential geoidal changes.

The geoid carries the mean sea level (MSL) and departures from the geoid are called the sea-surface topography (SST). In addition to the regular and predictable tidal components sea-surface topography is a function of dynamic effects associated with oceanographic, meteorologic and hydrologic factors. Ocean currents and variations in temperature, salinity and wind stress can cause changes of sea level of the order of decimetres. Variations in atmospheric pressure, precipitation and river discharge can cause changes of the order of centimetres. Generally these effects are amplified over continental shelves and in coastal waters compared with the open ocean. Under suitable circumstances the dynamic sea level can change by decimetres over distances of several kilometres. Some of the large scale features of SST, primarily oceanographic, are quasi-permanent with respect to time and space. However, meteorologic and hydrologic features of SST can vary on timescales of hours and days.

An example of a shallow water short timescale SST feature of special significance to the coastal engineer is the storm surge, which can be either positive or negative. Positive surges occur when low atmospheric pressure combines with wind, essentially onshore in direction, to produce exceptionally high tides which can threaten flooding in low lying areas. Negative surges can occur with a combination of wind, essentially offshore in direction, and high atmospheric pressure to produce lower than predicted tide levels which may restrict the passage of deep draught ships in shallow waters and channels. Areas particularly susceptible to the more catastrophic positive surge include the Bay of Bengal during the passage of tropical cyclones and the North Sea associated with the passage of deep depressions.

The North Sea experiences, on average, five surges each year with magnitudes up to 1 m. However, the theoretical maximum surge is close to 4 m which compares with the 3 m associated with the 1953 surge which caused disastrous flooding and considerable loss of life on the East Coast of England and in Holland. These surges are often associated with intense depressions moving from the Atlantic into the North Sea. While the depression is over the eastern Atlantic a small positive surge develops on the west coast of Britain due to strong south-westerly winds forcing water towards the shore. At the same time a small negative surge develops on the western side of the North Sea due to the same winds. However as the depression moves across Britain, in the 1953 case across central Scotland, and out over the North Sea the wind veers and becomes north-westerly. A positive surge results as water is forced south along the east coast of Britain, reinforced by the arrival of the positive surge from the west coast, and together these amplify the high tide travelling in the same direction (ie. from north to south, anti-clockwise around the North Sea amphidromic system). The funnelling effect of the basin means that the maximum effect of the surge is experienced in the south-western corner of the North Sea which can be reinforced by the extreme low pressure associated with the central areas of the depression. Early warning of surges is now possible if accurate meteorological data is combined with computer models based on past surges and satellite tracking of storms.

Present trends of sea level can be established from the analysis of long-term records from tide-gauges. All recent major reviews of global sea level trends agree that mean ocean levels are indisputably rising and most are approaching a consensus view on the rate of change of between 1.1 and 3.0 mm/year (Carter, 1989). Barnett (1984) divides available long-term sets of records into groups representing different oceanic regions and concludes that there has been an average total rise of 14.3 +/- 1.4 cm between 1890 and 1980 or 1.59 mm/year. During the last fifty years this rate of change has risen to 2.3 mm/year. Peltier and Tushingham (1989) suggest a rate of 2.4 +/- 0.9 mm/year. In another global review of records from 247 tide-gauge stations Emery (1980) was able to show an average annual increase in relative sea level of 3 mm/yr with a variation of +/- 13 mm/yr. The latter figure suggests that tectonic, isostatic and dynamic factors probably dominate eustatic factors in many parts of the world at the present time.

Emery et al (1985) discuss records from 134 tide-gauge stations in European seas, all of which had a minimum of 10 years duration. This data was subject to eigenanalysis which allowed for the rejection of aberrant records, the use of records from stations having different but overlapping time spans and the inclusion of stations which had gaps in the record. The resulting map, based on data for the period 1924 to 1980, is shown in Figure 3.3.

The fact that maximum rates of relative uplift in northwest Europe occur in Scandinavia and Scotland suggests that there is still a major component of isostatic rebound associated with former ice sheets in these two areas. The sinking of southern England and western France could, in part, be related to the continued collapse of a former fore-bulge associated with the same ice bodies but other tectonic factors may also be of importance. Carter (1982,1988) in discussing the case of the British Isles arrives at essentially the same conclusion. The maximum range of relative movement over the region is around 16 mm/year which is larger than present global eustatic trends.

**Future sea level change**

There are many possible responses and feedbacks of the Earth's physical and biological systems to the projected global warming. Of direct significance in terms of coastal environments is that global warming may significantly increase the global eustatic component of relative sea level rise primarily through enhanced melting rates of existing polar ice sheets and thermal expansion of the world's oceans.

Several estimates of the rates and magnitudes global sea level rise

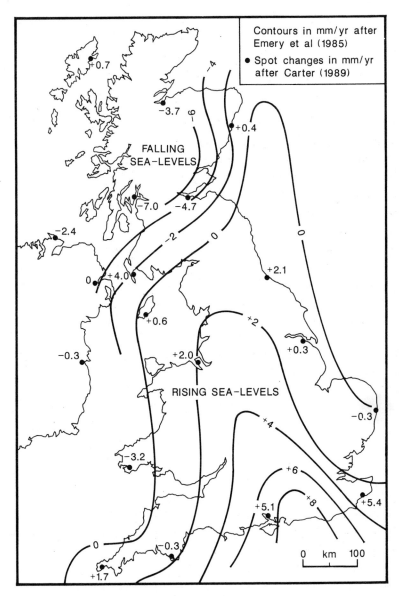

**FIGURE 3.3 PRESENT SEA LEVEL
TRENDS IN BRITAIN**

*Greenhouse effect and rising UK sea levels*

over the next century are available in the literature. A recent projection by Van Der Veen (1989) suggests a global rise of 22-66 cm by 2085 at a rate 4-6 times greater than measured over the last century. A particularly thorough and rigorous treatment of potential sea level rise is given by Hoffman (1984).

Several scenarios of sea level change, related to ice cap melting and thermal expansion of the oceans, are developed on the basis of alternative models and assumption regarding future changes in atmospheric composition and climatic response. Variations allowed for in terms of atmospheric composition include predictions of future $CO_2$ emissions based on economic forecasts and possible alternative energy production strategies, the fraction of $CO_2$ which remains in the atmosphere based on assumptions regarding the carbon-cycle and the possible increases in concentrations of trace gases.

In addition to the direct effect of increased greenhouse gases in the atmosphere several possible climatic "feedbacks" were also incorporated into the models. These included the enhanced ability of a warmer atmosphere to retain more water vapour which is a very effective greenhouse gas in it's own right. Global warming will also reduce the earth's albedo by reducing the highly reflective snow and ice cover. Cloud cover could reduce and average cloud height could increase, each leading to enhanced global warming.

A further complication in modelling climatic response is the possible uneven distribution of warming over the surface of the Earth. Most projections (for example Hansen et al 1984) suggest that polar regions of the world will experience substantially greater increases of temperature than the average, perhaps by as much as 2-3 times, with obvious implications for ice cap melting.

Various assumptions regarding ocean and glacial responses to global warming were also built into the scenarios. Ocean response in terms of thermal expansion was modelled in terms of different heat diffusion coefficients with heat retained within the top 100 m of the water column.

Glacial response is particularly difficult to model since not all melt from glaciers will actually run off and changes in the availability of meltwater within the glacier may cause changes in flow regimes. Another complication is that increased precipitation in polar areas may actually lead to enhanced accumulation on glaciers (Budd, 1988). The approach adopted by Hoffman involved the assumption that there would be a continuation of the past association between thermal expansion and total sea level rise. Past estimates of the thermal contribution to sea level rise were assessed to determine the snow/ice contribution. The ratio of snow/ice contribution to thermal expansion can then be extrapolated into the future. Ratios adopted were either one-one or two-one. These assumptions are acknowledged as a particularly weak area in the development of the sea level change scenarios.

A further complication is related to uncertainties regarding the response of the marine based West Antarctic ice sheet to both warming and sea level rise. A positive feedback may occur in which the ice sheet may become unstable and subject to catastrophic collapse (Clark and Lingle, 1977). Should this happen it could add very significantly to global sea level rise, possibly by as much as 6 m, a component not included in the following scenarios.

The resulting sea level rise scenarios are shown in Table 3.1. The values presented are worldwide means which take no account of possible regional variations due to geoid adjustments related to changed distribution of mass. The credibility of these scenarios will be improved if the wide range of estimates are refined by research directed towards reducing uncertainties in the assumptions on which models are based (Shennan and Tooley, 1987).

Clark and Primus (1987) present an analysis of sea level changes associated with the melting of the Greenland and Antarctic ice sheets

## TABLE 3.1.

### ESTIMATED SEA LEVEL RISE (cm) BY
### VARIOUS SCENARIOS, 2000-2100
(Source: Hoffman, 1984)

| Year | Conservative | Mid-range Scenarios | | |
| | | Moderate | High | Very High |
|------|--------------|----------|------|-----------|
| 2000 | 4.8 | 8.8 | 13.2 | 17.1 |
| 2025 | 13.0 | 26.2 | 39.3 | 54.9 |
| 2050 | 23.8 | 52.3 | 78.6 | 116.7 |
| 2075 | 38.0 | 91.2 | 136.8 | 212.7 |
| 2100 | 56.2 | 144.4 | 216.6 | 345.0 |

(see also Table 5.1) which takes into consideration both glacio-isostatic and geoid adjustments due to changes in the distribution of mass over the surface of the Earth. Also considered is the possible tilting of coastlines towards the ocean basins in response to loading by additional water on adjacent continental shelves. The Greenland and Antarctic cases are considered separately but both produce a very uneven sea level change over the Earth's surface with maximum sea level rise in the centres of the oceans due to ocean floor sagging. Glacio-isostatic rebound around the two ice sheets results in sea level falls over considerable areas. The resulting estimates of sea level change are shown in Table 3.2 for specific locations.

The figures presented assume a 100 cm contribution to the world's oceans from each ice sheet. In other words the figures represent a percentage change for any particular eustatic contribution. The change at any locality will be the sum of the contributions from each ice sheet. As an example suppose that by the year 2100 Greenland contributes 25 cm and Antarctica contributes 80 cm to global eustatic rise then the actual rise at London would be 95 cm (25 percent of

*Global reactions of oceans and seas*

## TABLE 3.2

## SEA LEVEL CHANGES ON CONTINENTAL COASTLINES DUE TO MELTING OF GREENLAND AND ANTARCTIC ICE CAPS

(Source: Clark and Primus, 1987)

In each case it is assumed that eustatic sea level rise due to melting is 100cm. ie. these figures represent the percentage rise of any eustatic component.

| Location | Sea level rise (cm)(- = fall) Contributions from: | |
| --- | --- | --- |
| | Greenland | Antarctica |
| **NORTH AMERICA** | | |
| Louisiana | 91.2 | 115.8 |
| Anchorage | 69.4 | 117.2 |
| San Diego | 93.5 | 117.0 |
| Chesapeake Bay | 58.7 | 115.7 |
| **ASIA** | | |
| Bangladesh | 100.5 | 108.4 |
| Japan | 107.2 | 120.0 |
| **AFRICA** | | |
| Cape Town | 113.9 | 94.8 |
| Mauritania | 90.5 | 116.9 |
| Somalia | 104.6 | 110.5 |
| **SOUTH AMERICA** | | |
| Amazon Delta | 102.9 | 113.0 |
| Lima | 111.4 | 113.6 |
| Rio de Janeiro | 110.0 | 102.8 (cont.) |

*Greenhouse effect and rising UK sea levels*

EUROPE

| | | |
|---|---|---|
| Portugal | 57.6 | 115.4 |
| Netherlands | 30.4 | 109.4 |
| London | 22.9 | 111.3 |

AUSTRALASIA

| | | |
|---|---|---|
| Sydney | 115.0 | 96.4 |
| New Zealand | 117.3 | 89.7 |

POLAR AREAS

| | | |
|---|---|---|
| Spitzbergen | -98.1 | 113.9 |
| McMurdo | 110.0 | 123.0 |

22.9 and 80 percent of 111.3). These estimates do not include the thermal expansion component since this only involves changes in density and not changes in mass. As a guide Hoffman et al. (1983) suggest a likely scenario for the latter to be 72cm by AD 2100 with a range of estimates between 28 and 118 cm (see above). Clearly there can be little doubt that sea level is likely to rise at most locations around the world during the next century due to the greenhouse effect but equally clearly a major priority must be a reduction in uncertainty in the range of sea level change estimates. In addition considerable effort must be devoted to an assessment of the impact of predicted sea level changes on the world's coastlines.- The physical, social and environmental consequences of sea level rise can be broadly divided into shoreline retreat through enhanced erosion, an increased frequency of temporary and permanent flooding on coastal lowlands (particularly associated with storm surges) and salt intrusion into coastal aquifers (Titus and Barth, 1984). Secondary considerations include former landfill sites containing toxic wastes in coastal areas which may be activated by flooding or erosion. Clearly the responses to these threats could involve either prevention or mitigation. The eventual choice will depend on technical, economic and political considerations. However, it should be stressed that advance planning for sea level rise alone could mitigate some effects and could save vast sums of money for many countries with coastal lowlands.

# 4

# SEA LEVEL RISE

## D. T. PUGH

At a MAFF Conference in 1986 I made a statement about the problem of sea level rise. The factual position has changed little in the interim although public awareness and concern has increased dramatically. Essentially, global air temperatures have probably risen by about 0.5°C in the past 100 years; over the same period global sea levels have increased by between 10-15 centimetres. There is no evidence for an accelerated rate of sea level rise.

However, a plausible series of scientific scenarios suggest that future sea levels will rise more rapidly as a result of greenhouse atmosphere warming. These links are the basis for current concern. Engineers need to establish clear rules as a basis for designing marine structures which have lifetimes of decades and longer. This short account presents one view of the actions which can be initiated or reinforced now, so that better planning information will be available in future. A fuller account is published elsewhere (Pugh, 1990).

### Possible Limits: Ice Effects

The first question to resolve is whether there is a natural limit to future sea level rise imposed by other constraints: there is a limit, but a high and unhelpful one! If all of the present grounded ice were to melt and the water released were distributed over the whole surface of the oceans, sea levels would increase by 88 metres. However, such a simple calculation is misleading because, for example, areas previously covered by ice will rise whereas those newly-supporting a heavier load of sea water will subside. This adjustment process takes place over several thousand years at a rate controlled by the physical properties of the earth's interior.

This readjustment is still underway in Britain following the removal of the ice load at the end of the ice age some 10,000 years ago. There is clear geological and other evidence of a gradual uplift of the north of Britain and a gradual subsidence in the south-east. The subsidence, which is much more serious for consequences of sea level rise is a result of the compensation, by small lateral flow within the earth's mantle, for the upward movement further north.

One of the problems when estimating global sea level rise is to allow for ice-loading effects. Recent calculations of global sea level rise which take into account estimated glacial loading effects at each gauge site (Peltier and Tushingham, 1989) suggests that the true rates of global sea level rise may be increased to about 25 centimetres a century. However, Stewart (1989) considers that the rise may be much less than this.

**Trends in UK Sea Levels**

There are several different sources giving direct or indirect evidence for sea level change. These include the distribution of erosion notches, raised beaches and salt water peats. Nevertheless, the most reliable evidence comes from direct measurements made by tide gauges, although few of these measurements extend back into the nineteenth century. The oldest British station is Sheerness (1832) but this record contains several breaks which can be interpolated by data from Southend across the Thames Estuary. The most reliable and systematic records have been taken continuously since May 1915 by the Ordnance Survey at Newlyn, Cornwall. Collection and analysis of sea-level data around the British Isles is now the responsibility of the Ministry of Agriculture, Fisheries and Food and the Scottish Development Department. The work is co-ordinated by the Natural Environment Research Council Proudman Oceanographic Laboratory on

Merseyside. Analyses of these records is not easy because many are of short duration and there are many gaps. At present only the records from Sheerness, Newlyn, Aberdeen and North Shields (Fig. 4.1) are sufficiently long for detailed analysis (Woodworth, 1987).

The resulting trends for sea level rise, relative to the local benchmarks, for the period 1916-1982 are:

| | |
|---|---|
| Newlyn | 1.78 +/- 0.11 mm per year |
| Aberdeen | 0.86 +/- 0.19 |
| Sheerness | 1.94 +/- 0.23 |
| North Shields (Tyne) | 2.61 +/- 0.24 |

## How may global warming be related to sea level rise?

These gradual increases have taken place without noticeable local difficulties; adjustment to gradual change seems to be acceptable. But the concern for the next century is based on something different: projections of future sea level rise as a response to enhanced greenhouse effects and global warming. Increases in the volume of water in the ocean are due to thermal expansion and due to mass increase as a result of the melting of grounded ice. Present knowledge does not allow us to distinguish between these two effects. If all of the ice in small glaciers were to melt, the equivalent rise in sea level is estimated at 0.3m. Polar ice melting is not considered to be a major net contribution to global sea level rise, although there may be some melting at the margins. Variations of the order of 0.05m in global sea levels could occur over century timescales due to irregular natural fluctuations in Antarctic precipitation.

## Predicting future sea level increases

Estimating likely future increases of global sea level over the next 100 years is a very uncertain process. The fact is that even the present

*Greenhouse effect and rising UK sea levels*

SEA-LEVEL (MM)

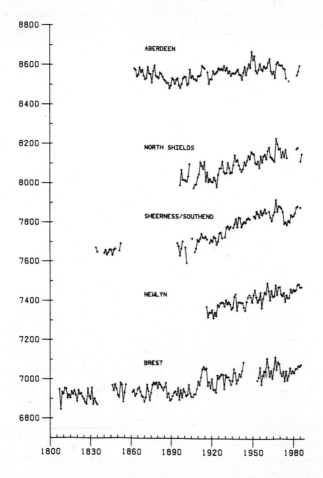

FIGURE 4.1  ANNUAL SEA LEVEL RECORDS
FROM THE FOUR MOST RELIABLE UK SITES.
- For comparison the much longer series at
Brest, France, is also included.
(Supplied by Permanent Service for Mean Sea
Level, Proudman Oceanographic Laboratory, Merseyside.)

*Sea level rise*

rise of sea level cannot be divided among the probable mechanisms with confidence. Nevertheless, many projections have been made. The more spectacular the prediction, the more likely it is to attract media attention. However, a UNEP Workshop held in Norwich in 1987 produced carefully argued estimates which have been adjusted only marginally since (Warrick and Wigley, in Press).

These conservative statements of sea level rise included an increase of 0.13 + / - 0.04 m to 2027, but the confidence limits are to be treated with extreme caution. By 2087, the Workshop, in its preliminary conclusions, suggested a lower limit of 0.61 m for sea level rise globally. This assumed no net contribution from melting polar ice, but it was recognised that this assumption was a major source of uncertainty.

For our four UK stations, allowing for local land movements, the projected increases are:

|  | 2027 | 2087 |
|---|---|---|
| Newlyn | 0.14m | 0.63m |
| Aberdeen | 0.09 | 0.51 |
| Sheerness | 0.16 | 0.69 |
| North Shields | 0.16 | 0.71 |

The effects of these estimated increases have been the subject of several detailed local impact studies, including some in Chapter 6. These studies are of great value in helping to identify the areas at risk and the scale of potential problems. But planners must not lose sight of the great uncertainty associated with these estimates. There can be no substitute for initiating or continuing high quality measurements of sea level, continuously as a basic ingredient of a monitoring system.

Another point to bear in mind when considering the vulnerability of a length of coast to the mean sea level changes tabulated above is that their effect on total flood levels will depend on the statistics of local meteorological surges and tidal level changes. For example, at Newlyn the present '100-year return' level will have become the '5-year return' level by 2027, whereas the present '100- year return' level at Sheerness will still have a relatively long return period of 60 years.

Another complication which cannot be fully considered at this stage is the effect of any climate change on the frequency and severity of meteorological storm surges. Further, changes in sea level may affect the way in which estuaries respond to tidal forcing, although these changes are likely to be of secondary importance.

## How do we make more reliable estimates ?

A proper understanding of sea level changes and their impacts requires monitoring, research and impact studies. The basic phenomena of sea level rise will be global in extent, but all impacts are, by definition, local.

One goal of the monitoring systems which must be developed will be the early detection of an accelerated rate of sea level rise above the 0.15 m or so per century which has been observed to the present.

However, the early detection of accelerating rates of sea level rise against the year-to-year variability will be difficult, and the local vertical land movement is an additional complicating factor. The World Ocean Circulation Experiment (1990-95) will help us understand the year-to-year variability and remove it from the observations. There is a close parallel here with changes in atmospheric pressure; high and low sea level systems exist in the oceans. The ocean currents flow around these in the same way that winds blow around high and low centres of atmospheric pressure.

Incidentally some enthusiasts for sea level rise have looked at five or so years of sea level measurements and projected these to predict vast increases in the near future. This is as unreal as calculating an increase in the mass of the atmosphere just because the barometer rises.

Annual sea levels are affected by average atmospheric pressures (Pugh, 1987) according to the 'inverse barometer effect' whereby a millibar increase in atmospheric pressure reduces the sea level by a centimetre. Corrections for this direct effect can also help to clean up the annual mean sea level signals so that an accelerated rise may be more easily detected.

We need to improve our understanding of the physics which links climate change with sea level rise. Even on the basis of plausible scenarios some modest expenditure may be justified as an insurance premium. But direct observations of rise are necessary before vast programmes of economic and social adjustment can be justified and accepted.

Global activities in which the UK can participate include:

1. Development of the Global Sea Level Network (GLOSS) (Fig. 4.2) under the auspices of the Intergovernmental Oceanographic Commission (IOC, 1990). The Permanent Service for Mean Sea Level, Directed by Dr. Philip Woodworth at the Proudman Oceanographic Laboratory, has international responsibility for collection, analysis, publication and interpretation of global sea level measurements.

2. Connection of several selected gauges in this network to an absolute geocentre reference system (Carter et al, 1989) so that vertical land movements can be distinguished from changes in sea level. This will require a combination of Very Long Baseline

58

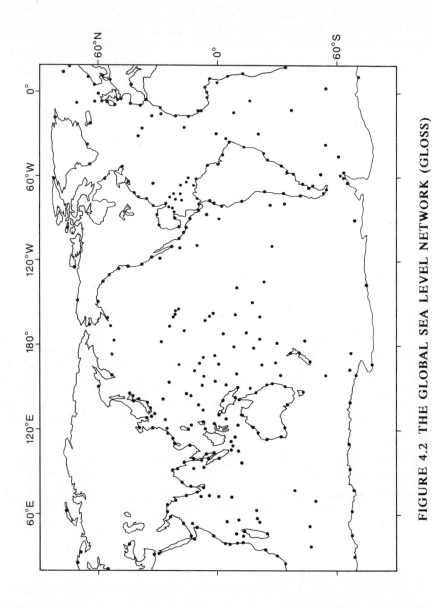

FIGURE 4.2 THE GLOBAL SEA LEVEL NETWORK (GLOSS)

*Sea level rise*

Interferometry, the satellite Global Positioning System, Lunar and Satellite Laser Ranging, and absolute gravity measurements.

3. Research on the underlying physical processes relating global warming to sea level rise should focus on the way in which the oceans will absorb extra heat and expand, and the melting of marginal ice in the polar regions.

Activities specifically directed to UK effects include:

1. The existing UK National Tide Gauge Network (Fig. 4.3) must be maintained and strengthened; additional gauges could be operated to the same standards in areas known to be at risk.

2. These gauges should also be connected at 5 or 10 year intervals into a geocentre coordinate system.

3. The data from these gauges should be analysed at intervals to determine:
   a) the effects of sea level rise on flood return periods at specific sites
   b) trends in high and low water levels which may be different from those of mean sea level
   c) trends in the frequency and severity of extreme flooding events

4. Even at this early stage it is useful to initiate a series of case studies, as has been done in several areas in the United States, to identify the most significant potential impacts and possible social and engineering responses in UK areas most at risk from sea level rise.

TIDE GAUGES OF THE NATIONAL NETWORK –DECEMBER, 1989

## FIGURE 4.3 THE UK SEA LEVEL MEASURING NETWORK OPERATED BY THE PROUDMAN OCEANOGRAPHIC LABORATORY ON BEHALF OF THE MINISTRY OF AGRICULTURE, FISHERIES AND FOOD

*Sea level rise*

## Conclusions

Sea level rise must be considered as only one component (and a tentative component) of the on-going problem of coastal zone management and protection. This general problem of coastal zone management is likely to be exacerbated in the decades ahead by increased pressure for coastal dwelling, particularly in developing countries. The whole problem of coastal management needs more observation and research to establish a sounder knowledge base. Designs should allow flexibility to adjust to changed scenarios as these develop.

The immediate needs are to install and maintain global and local sea level measuring networks for monitoring change, and to study the physical processes which link climate warming and sea level rise. There is an urgency to understand the processes and their consequences before irreversible changes, such as the melting of the West Antarctic Ice Sheets are accelerated. Over the next 20 years the problem is to establish a sound scientific and engineering capability for adjusting the sea level rises which may occur in the 21st century.

# 5

# EFFECTS OF SEA LEVEL RISE ON

# THE COASTAL ZONE

## I. H. TOWNEND

From a geological perspective the coastline is transitional and is rarely stationary for long. This results from the interaction of three factors (Gretener, 1988):
- sea level fluctuations
- uplift/subsidence
- sediment supply

These all tend to be episodic components with differing rates and operating over very different time-scales. Whereas glaciation will alter sea level over a period of $10^4$-$10^5$ years (see Chapter 3), the opening or losing of an ocean basin has a time scale of $10^8$ years. In addition, the varying magnitudes of these components means that the coastline may advance or retreat depending on the particular combination. For instance during a period of sea level rise, uplift or a high sediment supply can give rise to an advancing shore.

The lively current debate on global sea level rise as a consequence of the "greenhouse effect" has brought this topic to the fore. In order to be able to plan and manage within the coastal zone an appreciation of how the coastal environment will respond to sea level rise is required.

With respect to coastal hydrodynamics and morphology there is already an extensive literature, although there remain several aspects where our knowledge of how things will be affected is still extremely limited. The following sections provide a brief review of some of the key aspects. Of relevance to the engineering community is the likely influence on coastal structures and this is examined by way of some examples. To conclude, the problem is related to the overall requirements of coastal management.

## Sea level

Sea levels are dependent on a combination of global and local effects. The most important factors are:

- the total amount of water in the oceans
- the variations in water temperature through depth, which influence the density and hence the volume of the water mass
- the shape (bathymetry) of the ocean floors.

There will then be local variations in the rate of change of sea level, as shown in Chapter 3, as a consequence of influences such as winds, currents and land subsidence or emergence.

### Future Predictions

To estimate global sea level rise, the various processes must be modelled and the interactions of man-made and natural systems accounted for. Unfortunately, the existing scientific knowledge is not yet sufficient to make accurate predictions. Consequently it is necessary to consider a range of estimates, derived by assessing the possible variations for each assumption that has to be made. These estimates provide a reasonable basis for assessing planning options and for developing designs because, despite the uncertainties, they remain the best information currently available.

The US Environmental Protection Agency (Hoffman et al, 1983 and 1985) have published a range of estimates for high and low scenarios, covering the period 1980 to 2100. The composition of these estimates, with contributions due to thermal expansion and various elements of ice-melt, is summarised in Table 5.1 (see also Table 3.1). More recent work at the University of East Anglia (Warrick et al, 1989) has shown slightly lower estimates over the period 1985 - 2050 (Fig. 5.1). It is these estimates that form the background to the rest of this chapter.

Given the uncertainties associated with the estimates of polar melting and break-up, it is interesting to examine their relative importance. Table 5.1 shows that for the period to the year 2000, they represent a negligible proportion of the predicted rise. By the year 2050 they comprise 27 % of the total estimate and by 2100 they are the major

### TABLE 5.1

### ESTIMATED CONTRIBUTIONS TO SEA LEVEL RISE

| CAUSE | Sea Level Rise (mm) | | | | | |
|---|---|---|---|---|---|---|
| | 1980 - 2000 | | 1980 - 2050 | | 1980 - 2100 | |
| | low | high | low | high | low | high |
| Thermal expansion | 22 | 34 | 119 | 260 | 285 | 828 |
| Alpine melting | 12.5 | 20 | 57 | 138 | 123 | 372 |
| Greenland ice-cap melting | 0.5 | 1 | 12 | 39 | 62 | 268 |
| Antarctic ice-sheet break-up | 0 | 0 | 16 | 111 | 117 | 2205 |
| TOTAL | 35 | 55 | 204 | 548 | 587 | 3673 |

*Greenhouse effect and rising UK sea levels*

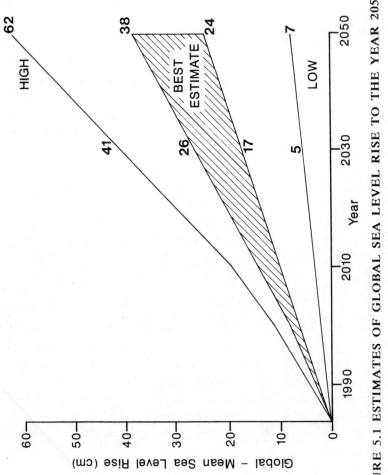

FIGURE 5.1 ESTIMATES OF GLOBAL SEA LEVEL RISE TO THE YEAR 2050

(Warrick et al, 1989)

*Effects of sea level rise on coastal zone*

influence amounting to some 67% of the total. Thus in essence polar melting and break-up is only likely to become significant in the period beyond 2050.

## Applications to the UK coast

As noted earlier (Chapter 3) the estimates of global sea level rise need to be adjusted for local effects such as land subsidence or uplift. This has been done here for four sites around the Anglian coast and predicted rises have been related to local tidal conditions for each site. The resultant predictions for the rise in the Highest Astronomical Tidal level are shown in Figure 5.2 (similar predictions could be developed to illustrate the potential rise in extreme water levels). Whilst the figure is useful for assessing local impact, it must be recognised that such rises in sea level may be accompanied by changes in currents, prevailing winds and storminess, as well as crustal warping due to redistribution of mass away from the polar regions. All these factors may produce additional local variations to the estimates.

## Coastal hydrodynamics

There are two aspects to the way in which normal and extreme events including waves, current and water levels may be affected. The first is that the climatic changes associated with the greenhouse effect may alter the "storminess" of a particular sea area. This could be as a result of deeper depressions or some shift in the general tracking of depressions. As yet such changes have not been directly associated with the greenhouse phenomenon, but various workers have suggested that wave heights in the North Sea and North Atlantic are increasing (Rye, 1976; Lamb and Weiss, 1979; Neu, 1984; Carter and Draper, 1988). The second aspect is the manner in which rising sea level alters the magnitude of the hydrodynamic processes.

FIGURE 5.2 PREDICTED SEA LEVEL RISE AT:
a.) Skegness    b). Harwich

*Effects of sea level rise on coastal zone*

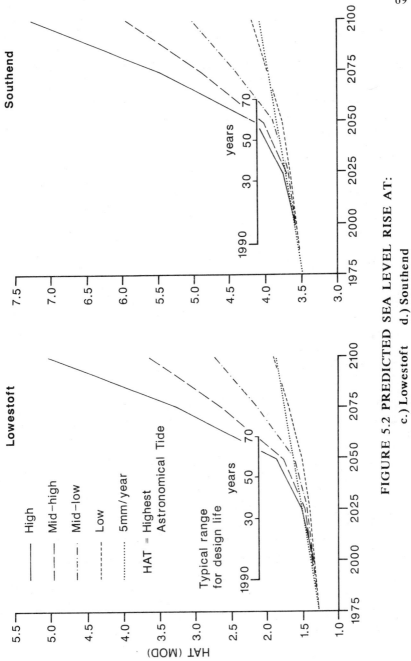

FIGURE 5.2 PREDICTED SEA LEVEL RISE AT:
c.) Lowestoft    d.) Southend

*Greenhouse effect and rising UK sea levels*

**Waves**

Increased water depths mean that waves are less likely to feel the bottom, so that frictional damping will be reduced. In addition wave generation over a given fetch will be enhanced again because of reduced bottom friction. An assessment of these two mechanisms (see NRC, 1987) suggests that a one metre rise in sea level will lead to increases of 3% and 7% respectively. In some but not all situations these increases may be linearly additive leading to an overall enhancement of some 10%.

**Tides**

Where water depths increase this could allow the tidal wave to propagate faster, thus altering currents and levels. However, changes in sedimentation may counteract this, so that there is little change in the tidal characteristics. In general where a shoreline is exposed to a deep-ocean tidal regime it is unlikely to be affected. Shores within basins such as the North Sea and Irish Sea may be subject to more noticeable effects due to the more complex interactions of the tidal components.

It is important to recognise that conditions are not necessarily in a steady state. Some 8000 years ago the water level in the North Sea was over 30 metres lower than at present. The basin was divided in two, with a land connection from North Norfolk to Texel in Holland. Since that time the coastline has changed extensively as sea level rose and clearly the tidal patterns will also have evolved. The active coastal processes on this east coast of England, exhibit a steepening of the cohesive beaches (Wakelin, 1989) as well as a resonance of the retreat rates along the coast (Townend and McLaren, 1989). These phenomena suggest that the tidal processes are not in equilibrium and that the basin is still evolving.

*Effects of sea level rise on coastal zone*

## Surges

The increase in water level caused by wind stress and barometric pressure gradients is likely to be most affected by variations in storm pattern as discussed above. However, for given conditions, an increase in sea level will also extend the area of the mild offshore slope, leading to an increase in surge elevations. The exception is where the shelf is of uniform depth, where an increase in water depth may result in a reduction in the wind induced surge (NRC, 1987).

## Coastal response

As noted at the beginning of this chapter, coastal response is a complex interaction of sea level, uplift/subsidence, and the availability of sediment. Existing morphological features will therefore respond differently according to the local conditions. For instance in Scotland isostatic rebound has resulted in wave-cut platforms being stranded, despite sea level rise. In Holland the large supply of sediment from the Rhine and Scheldt have in the past formed a series of prograding barriers despite the on-going (albeit small) rise in sea level at the time. In contrast many barrier beaches around the UK exhibit signs of overwash and roll back as the barrier tries to maintain its elevation relative to sea level.

There is a considerable literature on the development of the various coastal morphological forms; which have always depended upon sea level fluctuations as one of the contributory variables. More recently many authors have reviewed the response of present-day coastlines to sea level rise (Carter, 1988; Orford, 1987; NRC, 1987; Clayton, 1989b) and studied in detail particular aspects of the response such as beach profile adjustment (Bruun, 1988); cliff recession (Dalrymple, 1986; Clayton, 1989b) and marsh sedimentation (Reed, 1988). The following merely highlights a few points of interest.

### Beaches

It is widely reported that non-cohesive beaches exhibit an equilibrium profile (Bruun, 1954; Dean, 1987; Vellinga, 1984) which has been shown to equate to uniform wave energy dissipation across the surf zone (Dean, 1977). As sea level rises the beach profile is translated shorewards, with recession of the upper beach and deposition on the lower flatter slope. This effect can be illustrated by applying a storm erosion model to a typical east coast profile and progressively raising the water level (Figure 5.3). This, however, only accounts for the 2-dimensional response and it is necessary to compute a full sediment budget to ensure the proper application of the "Bruun rule" (Bruun, 1988).

For cohesive shores, which may comprise a sand veneer beach overlying a clay sub-base the situation is less clear. On the Great Lakes extensive measurements over the last century suggest that these cohesive shores also exhibit an equilibrium profile (Philpott, 1984). Again this has been related to uniform energy dissipation across the surf zone (Nairn et al, 1986). Recent work on the east coast of the UK has noted that the cohesive beaches are steepening as well as retreating (Townend and McLaren, 1989). The notable difference between the Great Lakes and the UK east coast is that there is no tidal range on the Lakes, whereas there are substantial tides in the Thames estuary and along the Norfolk, Lincoln and Holderness shores. This means that downcutting of the clay sub-base is able to take place more uniformly across the profile, rather than being concentrated at the top of the profile. In consequence there is greater horizontal retreat at low water than at high water.

As sea level rises, the greater water depth is likely to reduce shear stresses at the bed and hence the downcutting on the lower portion of the profile. Thus the rate of beach steepening is likely to be reduced. The rate of horizontal retreat will however continue. Indeed,

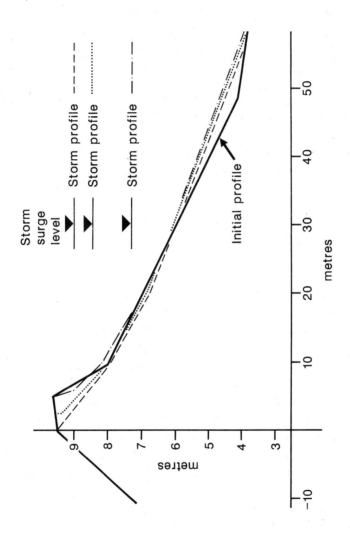

**FIGURE 5.3 MODEL PREDICTIONS OF BEACH EROSION DURING A STORM FOR PRESENT AND INCREASED STORM SURGE LEVELS.**

higher water levels may lead to more direct attack and increased reflection from cliffs at the top of beaches resulting in faster retreat rates.

### Tidal Inlets

A rise in sea level will tend to increase the tidal prisms of tidal inlets. This is because of reduced friction at the mouth and (potentially) a greater flooded area as a result of inundation within the inlet. Where the entrance of the inlet is constrained, the channel may get deeper in order to maintain equilibrium and as a consequence may reduce the stability of any structures present. Where there are ebb of flood tidal deltas (such as Blakeney on the Norfolk coast), an increase in the tidal prism may increase the storage volume of these shoals. This implies that any natural by-passing will be reduced, such that down-drift erosion increases.

### Marshes and Saltings

In general marsh plants are attuned to a particular mean water level. The distribution of a particular plant species can therefore be expected to move proportionally landwards as sea level rises; presuming of course that it has the freedom to do so. Experience in the US suggests that safeguarding the marshes may prove difficult, even with legislation in place (OTA, 1984).

Barrier beaches provide a dynamic sea defence, which can be expected to "roll-back" as sea level rises. As the barrier migrates this may reduce the area of the marsh behind unless the marsh is also able to migrate landwards. In certain areas this may require the abandonment of existing defences in order to give the marsh room to respond.

In the more quiescent water of the estuary there are often extensive saltings to be found. Providing there is an adequate sediment supply,

*Effects of sea level rise on coastal zone*

vertical accretion takes place. This has been found to occur at a rate exceeding increases in sea level in both the UK and USA (Reed, 1988; NRC, 1987).

Historically, natural losses of the marsh areas have not been reported and indeed there have been national gains. However, erosion of the marsh fringes over the last few decades has been reported at a number of UK sites. This may be due to a variety of reasons, such as lack of sediment supply, a readjustment of the marsh to sea level rise as it tries to migrate landward, or a short-term variation in the long-term trend. A better understanding of the various influences is required if the recent deterioration of the saltings is to be satisfactorily countered.

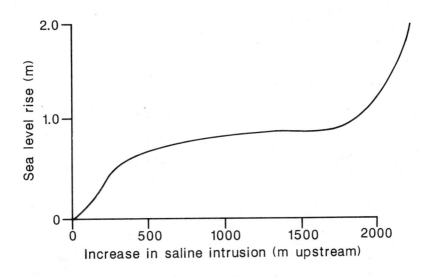

**FIGURE 5.4 PREDICTION FOR THE INCREASED DISTANCE OF SALINE INTRUSION ON THE RIVER TRENT USING THE 1-D ADVECTION DIFFUSION MODEL, STYX.**

*Greenhouse effect and rising UK sea levels*

There will also be a number of influences further upstream from the existing mouth. As sea level rises, saline intrusion will migrate further inland. Some predictions for the River Trent, using a one-dimensional advection diffusion model (STYX) with typical tidal conditions, suggests significant migration as mean sea level rises from 0.5 to 1.0 metres above the present day level (Figure 5.4). Such saline intrusion will lead to the eventual dominance of higher salt-tolerant plants, providing the transition is gradual. A rapid change (as suggested for the rise from 0.5 to 1.0 in Figure 5.4) could simply lead to loss of marsh. Increased intrusion will also influence coastal aquifer and freshwater intakes (Titus, 1986 and 1987).

### Coastal works

In addition to continuing change on the natural coast, the influence and effectiveness of coastal structures will also be altered as sea level rises. Thus when reviewing existing structures or designing new ones due account must be taken of the forecast rise.

It is already common practice to include an allowance for the secular rise in sea level as part of the design procedure. For the Anglian coast this would typically be some 2-4 mm/year over the design life of the project. Given that the forecasts predict an acceleration in the rate of sea level rise it would seem prudent to increase this allowance slightly. The plots in Figure 5.2 show a linear increase of 5 mm/year plotted against the range of forecast sea level rise scenarios. It can be seen that for the typical design life (30-70 years), this provides a middle of the range allowance, which tends towards the low forecast by the end of a long design life. Set against the possibility of any particular sea level rise scenario actually happening and the economic advantages of not incurring expenditure until necessary, such an allowance provides a reasonable trade-off.

An alternative option is to make provision for future raising or modifications. This can avoid reconstruction and is likely to be

*Effects of sea level rise on coastal zone*

particularly appropriate for schemes with a high initial capital cost.

### Groins

These structures have found extensive use around the UK. They are
intended to reduce the longshore drift of material and if wave heights
at the shore increase (see above) the longshore potential can be
expected to increase. The main requirement therefore will be to
maintain the level of the beach relative to sea level, which may
require some raising of the groynes. However, the life of these
structures is generally short and this is unlikely to present a particular
problem.

### Walls, Revetments, Embankments

All of these structures endeavour to hold a fixed line. Where there
is a backshore in front of the fixed line, which is able to supply the

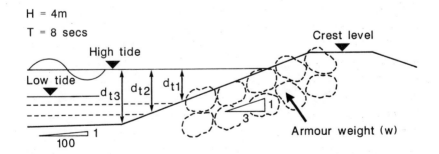

**FIGURE 5.5  DEFINITION SKETCH FOR
WORKED EXAMPLE**

*Greenhouse effect and rising UK sea levels*

sediment required for profile adjustment as the beach retreats landward, such structures are unlikely to have a marked influence. Ultimately, however, the backshore will be lost and this will be replaced by beach lowering immediately in front of the structure.

The performance of these structures will also be altered. As water depths in front of a seawall increase, so the extent to which wave conditions are depth limited is modified. This can have a pronounced effect on the wall's performance in terms of run-up/overtopping and

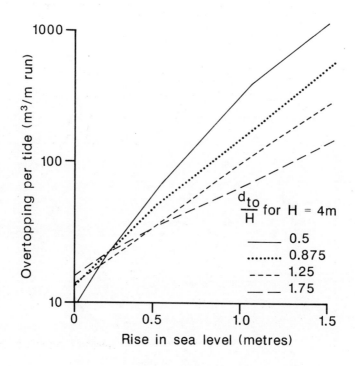

**FIGURE 5.6 INCREASE IN VOLUME OF OVERTOPPING PER TIDE**

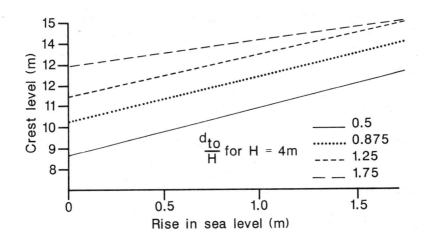

**FIGURE 5.7 INCREASE IN CREST LEVEL REQUIRED FOR A FIXED OVERTOPPING RATE OF 0.002 m³/sec**

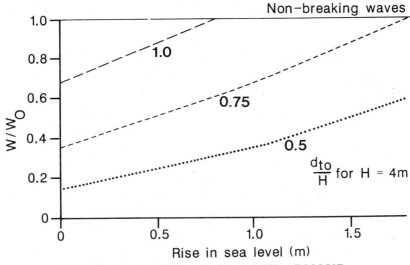

**FIGURE 5.8 INCREASE IN ROCK ARMOUR WEIGHT**

the stability of any armour units. To illustrate this some values for the example outlined in Figure 5.5 are presented in Figures 5.6 - 5.8. The overtopping calculations are based on the work of Owen (1980) and the rock armour weight as a proportion of the weight for non-breaking conditions (W/Wo) uses the equations of van der Meer et al (1986). The changes are most pronounced where wave conditions are strongly depth limited for the given exposure. Indeed, the crest levels required to maintain the design standard for overtopping increases more rapidly than the simple rise in water level under such conditions (a 0.5 m rise in sea level leads to a 1.0 m rise in crest level for the given example).

The situation may well be further exacerbated by increases in wave heights and surge/tide levels as outlined above.

### Beach Nourishment

The influence of a storm on a typical beach profile is illustrated in Figure 5.3. As can be seen there is increasing loss of sediment from the upper beach, which will also make beach recovery significantly more difficult. As a consequence there will be a need for greater volumes of beach fill, if a fixed line is to be maintained. Some estimates based on increased losses due to enhanced wave activity, suggest that fill requirements may increase by around 30% if sea level rises 1 metre (NRC 1987). Alternatively one could use progressively coarser material for future beach nourishment operations.

### Offshore Breakwaters

The design life of an offshore breakwater is usually 50-100 years which suggests that in future they will need to be designed for the possible scenarios of sea level rise, or with provision for future modification. The change in performance will be similar to the case of the simple seawall described above, with increased overtopping and a requirement for heavier armour units. In addition, unless the

*Effects of sea level rise on coastal zone*

shoreline is fixed, the distance to the shore will increase, so reducing their effectiveness.

## Management implications

The need for regional studies as a basis for coastal management is now more widely accepted and adopted (Townend 1986). To some extent this is a result of the tools now available to handle the large amounts of information that studying extensive lengths of coast inevitably entails (Fleming and Townend, 1989). Whilst the response to sea level rise has been considered in general terms by many authors (Titus, 1986 and  1987; Carter 1987 and 1988; Clayton, 1986b), there have only been a few site specific case studies within the UK (Clayton, 1989a; Shennan and Tooley, 1987). There is thus a need for impact plans as an  extension to regional studies in order to provide an  adequate evaluation of the options in a timely fashion. Research work  underway at a number of  UK institutions as part of an EEC funded  project, is seeking to develop a standard methodology for such impact plans. In the meantime some of the guidelines identified in Chapter 9 may provide a basis for local decision making. Those involved in the protection  of coastal communities will have to weigh the costs of retreating against the costs of maintaining  the current coastline. Whilst in some cases it will be necessary to accommodate the forecast rise  in future designs, elsewhere the community's exposure to the consequences of future sea-level rise will have to be met by consideration of a wider range of policy options.

The primary policy option with respect to sea-level rise requires the concerted action of the international community, to reduce the emission of greenhouse gases. On a local scale the policy options must address the economic costs and benefits of management actions. The possible courses of action will fall into one of four categories:

- maintain existing line        - retreat
- set-back                      - advance

The first option applies to any existing defence line and will generally be the preferred option wherever there is a  substantial investment in infrastructure on the coast. On an eroding coast, setting back can mean that it is only necessary to defend against tidal inundation. This option can also be used to provide natural features "room to  move" whilst retaining a level of defence against flooding. The retreat option is a managed withdrawal, allowing the coast  to return to its natural state and is an attractive option where the tidal flood plain is relatively narrow.  Finally, the advance option is included to acknowledge the possibility of limiting low-lying exposure by suitable reclamation or the use of tidal barriers.

The implementation of these various options will require a combination of engineering, ecological management, and  social  planning. These differing elements will need to be accommodated in coastal management plans, which acknowledge the coastal zone as a dynamic and transitional interface between land and sea. In the long term it may be  appropriate to consider moving whole communities, and such action may require new legislation. As such this needs to be addressed as a national issue.

## Conclusions

Clearly more  precise  estimates  of  future  sea level rise  would be helpful. However, it must be recognised that the  uncertainty  with respect to future sea level rise is no greater than the uncertainties associated with economic  growth, storm severity and other similar factors which have to be addressed as part of the coastal planning process. Furthermore, many scientists are of the view that it will take several years, and far more research, to substantially  improve on the forecasts currently available. It is therefore necessary to plan  using the available estimates, whilst recognising that there are uncertainties and that these become increasingly significant for longer term projections.

The problem of predicting future sea level rise is now recognised as an international research theme. There are a wide range of research projects underway and coastal managers and engineers need to review the results of these endeavours as they become available. Equally they will need to keep abreast of studies which consider the interaction between global and local sea level change entailing nationally organised monitoring associated with appropriate research projects.

There are, however, two areas where coastal managers should take initiatives. The first is to monitor the actual impact on the coast. Such monitoring is implicit in a management approach where data for key parameters is collected on a regular basis. The second initiative should be to examine the potential impact of the various forecast scenarios for planning purposes. Such studies will need to examine how each of the various services provided by the managing authority are likely to be affected. Inevitably this will need to interact with government and the development of a national policy for issues related to sea level rise. The most complex and controversial issue is likely to be the displacement of coastal communities, particularly where this relates to the maintenance of the coastal ecosystems (such as coastal wetland) as much as front line coastal defences. There is, therefore, a need for government to provide guidance on the policy and/or legislation to be enacted on this issue.

Finally, new designs should make an allowance for future sea level rise. This can either be in the form of including some measure of the predicted rise in design calculations, or by developing schemes which have the flexibility to be modified in the future. For the former option a rate of 5 mm/year is suggested as a good compromise. The final choice should however reflect the design life and the benefit/-cost streams of a particular scheme.

84

## Acknowledgements

I am grateful to John Wicks who provided the estimates of saline intrusions and also to Pauline Mullen and Marianne Lavin who prepared the figures and text.

# 6

# LANDS AT RISK FROM SEA LEVEL RISE

# IN THE UK

## I. R. WHITTLE

Large areas of land in the UK have been at risk from the sea since time immemorial. The UK has a wide range of types of land set at an equally wide range of levels, from high mountains to protected land which can be as much as 6m. below sea level.

The topography of the UK owes everything to past ice ages which have, depending upon the stages of their life-cycle, affected sea levels. The retreat of the last ice age from the British Isles has been instrumental in causing a rise in sea levels of some 100 m. (Brunsden et al 1989).

Sea levels have dictated the composition and depths of the various soils over lying the bedrocks in valley floors. Their distribution has not been uniform and today surface soils range from coarse inorganic soils through clays and silts to organic soils at the other extreme.

Man has always been prepared, to the limit of his ability, to exploit the potential of any land and change it to suit his immediate needs. As a consequence of his actions, as shown in Chapter 2, he has now introduced the greenhouse effect and the likelihood of a consequential rise in sea levels.

As needs have arisen man has changed his environment in other ways. He has felled trees to clear land, excavated channels to drain land and to divert waters to drive mills for grinding corn, cutting timber, driving turbines, which in turn satisfy other needs, but in one activity he has been extremely active. He has recognised that the flat coastal

*Greenhouse effect and rising UK sea levels*

and river valley plains contain valuable and highly productive alluvial or peat soils. To exploit the potential of these soils for agricultural production he has had to protect the land from river flooding and has reclaimed land from the sea by building sea exclusion defences. Later as the sea deposited more material against the seaward side of the defences, and thus raised the level of these salt marshes, so man built yet another, but more seaward, defence.

Every few years the effectiveness of these defences is put to the test. Periodically an event occurs which is more severe than previously experienced and of sufficient severity to overwhelm, or cause a failure of, the defences.

The most far reaching events of this kind during the past century have been the river floods of 1947 and the tidal inundations of 1953. Since 1953 those sea levels have been exceeded on more than one occasion.

It is to the credit of flood defence engineers that damage has been limited and floods contained in localised areas. This containment has been due to the quality and standards of present day defences. Over the past 40 years drainage authorities, with government support, have thus secured and maintained adequate flood defence systems.

The question uppermost in many people's minds is whether these defences are adequate for the future. People fear that if forecasts of sea level rise are eventually proved correct, these low-lying lands will be at an even greater risk and the defences inadequate to provide protection.

By considering past events, analysing data and embarking upon monitoring programmes we can identify, in general terms, those lands at greatest risk. For the purposes of this chapter this identification has been limited to those lands lying below the 5m AOD(N) contour. To this outline has been added the 10m AOD(N) contour in order to

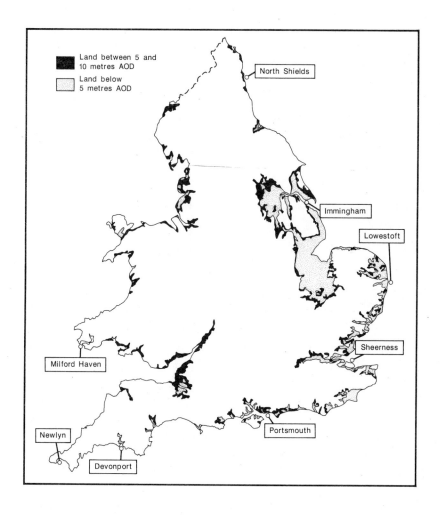

Land between 5 and
10 metres AOD

Land below
5 metres AOD

North Shields

Immingham

Lowestoft

Milford Haven

Sheerness

Newlyn

Portsmouth

Devonport

## FIGURE 6.1 LAND CLOSE TO SEA LEVEL

*Greenhouse effect and rising UK sea levels*

## TABLE 6.1

### SEA LEVEL TRENDS

| | Highest recorded level (m. AOD) | Level of mean high water spring tides (m. AOD) | Sea level trend in mm/year relative to local land datum | Standard error of trend (mm/yr) (+ or -) |
|---|---|---|---|---|
| North Shields | 3.57 | 2.4 | + 2.2 | 0.3 |
| Immingham | 4.78 | 3.4 | + 4.0 | 0.8 |
| Lowestoft | 3.35 | 0.9 | + 1.2 | 0.8 |
| Sheerness | 4.69 | 2.8 | + 2.4 | 0.3 |
| Portsmouth | 3.02 | 2.0 | + 4.1 | 0.6 |
| Devonport | 3.09 | 2.3 | + 0.8 | 0.7 |
| Newlyn | 3.28 | 2.6 | + 1.7 | 0.2 |
| Milford Haven | 4.49 | 3.3 | - 2.4 | 0.9 |

establish the extent of the "buffer zone". Generally this zone is quite narrow being limited by the series of escarpments in the hinterland. The justification for selecting these contours, whilst over-simplifying the argument, is demonstrated by considering tide gauge information (see Fig. 6.1).

It has been estimated that some 720,000 ha of agricultural land lies within the area bounded by the 5m contour. The land in the UK has been divided by MAFF into five classes of quality. Of the three highest classes only some 8% lies below 5m but a further analysis shows that some 198,000 ha (ie. 57%) of the highest grade land lies within this zone (Figs. 6.2 and 6.3).

*Lands at risk from sea level rise in UK*

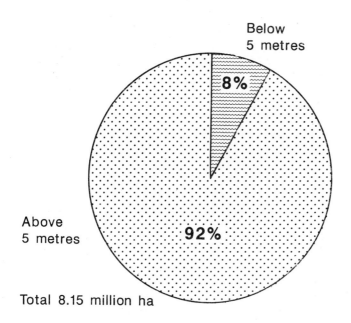

Below
5 metres

8%

Above
5 metres

92%

Total 8.15 million ha

FIGURE 6.2 GRADE 1-3 AGRICULTURAL LAND
IN ENGLAND AND WALES
IN RELATION TO THE 5 m CONTOUR

*Greenhouse effect and rising UK sea levels*

90

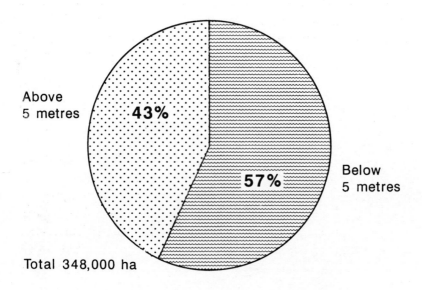

Above
5 metres

43%

57%

Below
5 metres

Total 348,000 ha

**FIGURE 6.3 GRADE 1 AGRICULTURAL LAND
IN ENGLAND AND WALES
IN RELATION TO THE 5 m CONTOUR**

*Lands at risk from sea level rise in UK*

Within this lower lying land is situated also many large residential and commercial areas, together with some of the most highly valuable chemical plants, power stations and other industrial areas of the UK.

Sea defences and tidal defences and possibly some coast defences combine to protect these low lying areas. The coastline of the UK is over 4000km long and whilst only 1000km are attributable to being classed as sea defences, there are another 800km of defences classed as coast protection defences. The asset value of these coastal defences has been put at between £4bn and £6bn. These analyses ignore tidal defences inland of the Schedule 4 boundaries (**Coast Protection Act 1949**).

There is ample evidence of the need to give some thought to the flood protection policies needed for the future.

The predictions for both rate of rise and extent of rise and the extent of any increase in storminess resulting from climate change are still unconfirmed. These uncertainties stem from the complexity of the global computations, the scarceness of relevant data and the limitations of predictive models currently available (Chapter 2). An attempt has been made to display these uncertainties (Fig. 6.4) but it may well be another decade before accurate computation can be made for areas around the UK.

Meanwhile, what policies should be considered for the protection of low-lying lands ? A fundamental requirement for all capital schemes is that they should be cost-effective. That is, the assessment of the benefits must exceed the cost of all the works. It is therefore a hard fact to accept, but it may well be so, that in future land protected at present will not always be given protection. This is not an original view and there are already many examples of the application of such a policy. In considering a protection policy, it is necessary to consider design concepts. One important assessment must be the life of

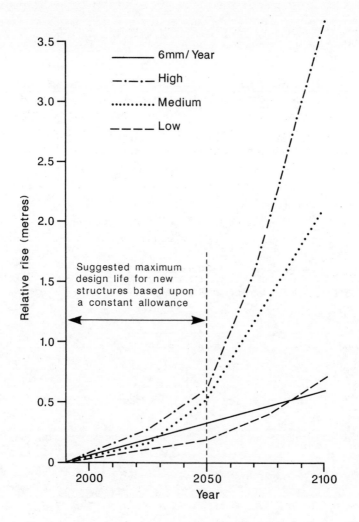

**FIGURE 6.4 RANGE OF PREDICTIONS FOR SEA LEVEL RISE
AT AN EAST COAST
PORT COMPARED TO AN ALLOWANCE OF 6 mm/year.**
(after Sir W Halcrow & Partn. Ltd.)

*Lands at risk from sea level rise in UK*

schemes, which is dependent upon many factors; primarily these are:

materials, exposure and dynamic loadings.

Generally, soft defences will have a shorter life than hard defences and because they may have to be reconstructed at an earlier date there is ample opportunity to modify any obsolete design criteria. It is the converse for solid defences so, at the initial design stage provision must allow for modifications to combat any obsolete criteria.

There is, of course, a policy worthy of consideration and which has to a great extent been neglected over the last few decades. Many low lying areas have been reclaimed form the seas and at each successive reclamation there were, and in places still are, remnants of those earlier defences. These could be reinstated, albeit at a low level, to provide second lines of defence. This compartmentalisation would limit flooding perhaps for a sufficiently long period to permit repairs to a breach in the main defence.

This policy is being adopted on the continent and may prove to be a cost-effective expedient in the UK.

Clearly, therefore, any policy must be prudently engineered but not be developed against a background of excess emotion or unconfirmed scientific knowledge.

**Note:**
The views expressed in this chapter are those of the author and do not represent the views of the Ministry of Agriculture, Fisheries and Food, for whom the author worked until recently as Chief Engineer, nor of the National Rivers Authority with whom he is now employed.

# 7

# THE GREENHOUSE EFFECT ON

# LOW - LYING LAND IN BRITAIN

## F. M. LAW

Sea level rise must have a subtle effect upon estuaries and the tidal rivers that feed them as brackish water moves further inland for longer durations. Intakes with no choice about timing and location of abstraction are most at risk. Embankment under-seepage will grow and back-ditch water will become more saline. Where saline reverse flows become trapped upstream of a fixed weir the impacts on abstractors and fisheries may be expected to be more noticeable. The dense saline wedge will also move further into coastal aquifers and where these are close to full development the effects could be dramatic if no avoiding action is taken. Precursors of anticipated 21st century conditions are on record due to previous tidal surges, old weak low embankments, over-pumping and tectonic changes. Appropriate contingency planning and higher drainage pumping budgets should ensure that life at the edge of Britain's freshwater resources remains viable in the best sense of that word.

Conditions will grow more complex where the freshwater regime is reducing concurrently and sediment load is high. It is possible that estuary deposition reaches will move upstream to such an extent that (in the absence of dredging) tidal river flood profiles are raised. However, in many cases higher winter flows would scour away any temporary problem and it is difficult to credibly suggest any scenario in which every factor is simultaneously adverse.

### Sensitive areas

Table 7.1 conveniently summarises the larger estuaries as defined by

## TABLE 7.1

## DISTANCE TO COAST FROM 1000 mg/l
## CHLORIDE LIMIT

| RIVER | KM | RIVER | KM |
|---|---|---|---|
| Tyne | 30 | Taw | 15 |
| Hull | 15 (to Humber) | Parrett | 30 |
| Trent | 15 (to Humber) | Bristol Avon | 15 |
| Nene | 30 (to Wash) | Severn | 40 |
| Great Ouse | 30 (to Wash) | (to Severn Bridge) | |
| Bure | 15 | Usk | 15 |
| Thames | 60 | Dee | 30 |
| Medway | 30 | Weaver | 35 |
| Sussex Ouse | 15 | (to Mersey Est.) | |
| Arun | 15 | Mersey | 40 |
| Hants. Avon | 20 | Douglas | 15 |
| (incl. S'ton water) | | (to Ribble Est.) | |
| Camel | 15 | Wyre | 15 |

*Footnotes*: *Data source is the IGS/BGS 625,000 scale Hydrogeological Map of England and Wales published by NERC 1977.*

*Data definition is the river length in which the chloride ion concentration is known to exceed 1000 mg/l under low flow conditions. The coast (except where shown) is taken as that determining the edge of the country on a small scale map and is necessarily an approximation.*

*Effect on low lying land in Britain*

a 1000 ppm chloride threshold. Comprehensive information is not so readily available for Scotland and Northern Ireland.

Table 7.2 details coastal fringe aquifers which are, or have been, substantially used by public and private sources and now exhibit the problems of saline intrusion. There is no such straightforward way of identifying flood prone areas in low-lying coastal areas. However, the various studies of possible estuary barrages around England and Wales are helpful in identifying potential problems of raised estuary levels.

## TABLE 7.2

## BRACKISH AQUIFERS AROUND THE ENGLISH COASTS

| LOCATION | APPROXIMATE DIMENSIONS | |
|---|---|---|
| | Coast Length (Km) | Depth (Km) |
| Hull | 10 | 5 |
| North Norfolk | 30 | 1 |
| East Norfolk | 85 | 10 |
| East London | 20 | 2 |
| Mersey | 40 | 5 |

## Saline intrusion up-river

A crucial feature of any estuary is where the deepest channel in its bed finally rises above high tide level. For example, it is only in relatively recent history that the dredging of the Thames has moved its saline sector so far upstream. It can be useful to visualise the tidal river as a reservoir to which the sea provides a moveable dam. Where its stored freshwater is large compared with the tidal volume changes it takes time for the effect of salinity to move upstream. But then if the inflow of freshwater drops away in drought the sea will move in to make up the shortfall.

In some estuaries the mix of factors will ensure a stratified flow with freshwater moving out seawards at the surface disguising a saline wedge creeping upstream in the opposite direction. Other estuaries will be inherently safer by exhibiting mixed conditions in any vertical profile so that the saline front is readily observed.

Worst conditions may not necessarily come from a run of spring high tides. It is necessary to keep an eye on periods when the absence of any really low tides allows the inexorable upstream creep of salinity to go on unchecked.

Several computer models are available of salinity movements within estuaries (Hydraulics Research Ltd., (HRL); Water Research Centre, (WRC); Institute for Marine Environment Research (IMER); Binnie and Partners, (B & P); Falconer) but all require successful calibration. This has been achieved for some UK estuaries (eg. Thames, Humber, Wash, Mersey, Severn, Tees, Wear, Lagan) but the cost of the field survey effort seems to have deterred many authorities from making that basic investment in understanding all their tidal rivers quantitatively. One technique, that of following up the high tide slack salinity past pre-defined cross-sections is a finely judged skill that can be very revealing if repeated in different flow and tide range combinations.

Computer runs after validation usually concentrate on steady-state circumstances such as low baseflow meeting a repeated spring tide cycle. This is useful for examining the range of the normal saline front and the way it will be drawn upstream by freshwater abstraction or be pushed back by regulation reservoir releases. However, fuller non-steady modelling of a complete season or year is more satisfying and gives warning of any accumulating problems.

Operation of marginal river intakes has a long history. The 1907 Act for Great Yarmouth's water supply restricted the Bure intake at Horning so that pumping ceased at a 286 ppm salinity limit. That intake was moved in 1970 from Horning to Belaugh to avoid salinity interruptions of the type experienced in the summer of 1935 and potentially in 1976; winter incursions occurred as well. It is reported that intake use even at Belaugh occasionally requires reduction by one third to avoid pulling the saline front up-river. A different example is the occasional diversion from the Trent to the Fossdyke Canal to back up the Witham-Ancholme industrial water supply scheme which has been required to avoid abstraction for 90 minutes either side of high tide.

### Associated impacts

Associated impacts include:

- brackish underseepage
- rapid drawdown slips
- impeded low tide drainage
- changed estuary flood profiles
- suspended sediment changes
- fixed weir capture of saline flow
- mobilisation of pollutants

It is not unknown for the back ditch in tidal embanked areas to be brackish from saltwater underflow and for this to cause interesting flora species diversity. Any rise in mean sea level must accentuate this seepage and bring forward the need for additional pumped drainage or flushing flows to prevent unwelcome side effects. By and large only small running cost increases are foreseen prior to the advent of bank raising schemes next century.

Where tidal range is accentuated, perhaps in the middle to upper reaches of present estuaries, it would not be surprising if rapid drawdown slips become more prevalent in both natural and man-made banks. In a few localities overtopping could follow on succeeding tides. With the worst scenarios land might be lost to agriculture completely. It is worth reflecting on Pagham Harbour, the nature reserve between Bognor and Selsey, which was reclaimed from the sea by sluice and embankment in the late Victorian era. However, not many years before World War I the sea over-topped the coastal embankment and the land has been lost to farming ever since.

Many areas depend for their effective flood drainage on a good low tide gradient and gravity drainage for sufficient hours/day. Amberley Wildbrooks on the tidal Arun is a well known example. Rising sea levels (and any continuation of a sinking south-east England) must advance the day when pumped drainage is needed or the Wildbrooks are allowed to be a degraded wetland. Those higher levels may well cause spring outlets to move inland in some localities with further accentuation of the need for improved artificial drainage.

The flood profile of many river systems are heavily dependent on the tidal regime to which they discharge. Geographic factors have led to occupation of the floodplain at the tidal limit crossing. Hence damage potential at such towns is high. A flurry of tidal flood barriers have been built in the last decade but their precursors can be seen in the Fens at sites such as Boston Grand Sluice and Denver Sluice on the Ely Ouse. As sea levels rise reviews will be needed of the performance of older sluices and their associated embankment systems. Non-steady state mathematical modelling of the type used for the River

Ancholme flood protection scheme will be particularly helpful in clarifying the risks that are currently being run and how these are changing.

Estuary siltation brings with it many practical problems. High sea levels seem bound to instigate suspended sediment movements into areas where they have been immaterial to date. Forewarning of the impact can be seen in the records of Wash tidal sluices in dry years where sediment has been deposited on the seawater face of gates to such an extent that they would not always open on the first autumn flood. Intermittent flushing releases were introduced to combat this and it would not be surprising if larger quantities were to be required in future. Silt movements on any scale trigger flood, ebb and navigation channel movements. There is a long and honourable history of dealing with such changes once they have begun but less success in being able to predict with certainty where and when they would occur. Here any growth in major freshwater flooding could also play its part.

Saline flows upriver can sometimes get over and then be trapped behind a fixed weir. This was an observed problem on the River Lune at Skerton Weir, possibly due to the gradual removal of tidal washland and funnelling of seawater upriver. There the industrial abstractions of five private firms and CEGB were at hazard in dry periods on high spring tides. The density gradients in the weir pool also had fishery implications. Because the Lune-Wyre transfer scheme lengthens the nett low flow period at Skerton, the weir was remodelled to reduce saline ingress and aid flushing. Similar works could be necessary on other rivers as and when sea levels rise. HRL showed that the McConnell Weir on the Lagan (Belfast) regularly traps seawater which de-oxygenates below the freshwater layer on the surface causing odours and related problems.

## Aquifer intrusion

The rainfall recharge of a permeable island in the ocean will form a lens of freshwater overlying denser saline water. The lens thickness rises in the wet season and falls in the drier weather that follows. Within the variations that occur over the years the edge of the lens will move out and back in response to any excess or deficiency of recharge over discharge. The Ghyben-Herzberg lens theory is the basis for most thinking about the response of coastal aquifers, even for complex larger islands like Britain.

As a handy rule the thickness of freshwater found below sea level will be 40 times that above sea level at the same point due to balancing the density differences. This presumes steady homogeneous conditions but naturally these are disturbed wherever there is a large tidal range and high aquifer permeability. Then a brackish zone will form at the interface and reduce the freshwater resource availability.

Where there have been landfills around coastal margins the rise of the water table consequent on sea level rise can be expected to accelerate leachate movement and methane generation. This is understood to have been foreseen as a limited problem by Wallace Evans and Partners in their Cardiff Bay barrage feasibility study.

Consider a simple case in which the coastline is formed of aquifer material without any river valleys through it. The natural discharge for the aquifer will be by springs close to sea level and by evaporation where the water table lies close to the surface on the coastline. Mathematical modelling will readily show the response of both the water table and the saline interface as seasonal recharge varies. More importantly it will show the marked changes that follow from borehole abstraction of a high percentage of recharge. The "cone" of depression in the water table causes the rise or "upconing" of the saline water beneath. Inevitably the lens contracts inland and the saline wedge advances towards the bores.

*Effect on low lying land in Britain*

Loss of coastal wells has happened in the past in Britain. In Eastbourne a high-yielding Upper Greensand well at Bedford was over-pumped at the end of the last century and drew in salt water. It was taken out of service and only after 50 years was the gradient reversed and the local aquifer flushed back to fresh conditions. Returning it to use required that a markedly lower draw-off rate be adopted. Presumably it was that experience which led Eastbourne Waterworks Company, with its Beachy Head Chalk wells and adits near sea level, to use monitor bores between source and sea. Pumping is trimmed to ensure that a net gradient seawards always exists. By contrast wells that went brackish in the 19th century at Bognor Regis, Littlehampton and Seaford have remained so (Headworth and Fox 1986).

It is understood that Anglian Water has in Norfolk been adopting a policy of moving the main aquifer pumping sites inland to reduce risks from saline intrusion as total usage of Chalk and Crag grows. Other well known coastal underground sources that have needed action to counter salinity risks are those around the Mersey estuary in Triassic Sandstone and on south Humberside in chalk. As far as is known the Durham coastline Magnesian Limestone sources have not proved difficult to manage in that regard. Southern Water Authority took over from Brighton Corporation a Chalk aquifer unit that has been seasonally pumped (ie. less severely at the coast in summer) in order to protect it from salinity. Bores by the Yorkshire Ouse at Selby have also had to be abandoned after over development drew in saline water (see JIWE Vol 27, 191 (1973)).

Climate change, as now visualised, may lead to slightly higher recharge due to a warmer wetter winter but with a longer summer recession season. If this is coupled with a sea-level rise then some coastal bores may go brackish in high tide periods of early autumn if operated traditionally. Most threatening would be a run of dry winters but there is no evidence from global circulation models yet that this should occur over Britain any more than it now can.

As has always been the case, the most crucial element in groundwater development is the percentage of recharge that is abstracted and consumed. Many British well fields have been promoted that were intended to abstract mean recharge without recognising (as surface storage designs do) that storage is finite and most vulnerable to runs of three or four dry years in unconfined aquifer units. Trimming pumping by 10 to 15% can soon cure a steady downward drift of the water table.

To use coastal bores for domestic consumption and then discharge the resulting effluent by outfall to the ocean gives no buffer to water-table impact (unless the distribution mains leak to the source aquifer). Borewater for irrigation is just as consumptive if it is efficiently done. Only in rural areas where septic tanks prevail is there recirculated recharge to mitigate the effects of intense use.

It is reasonable to foresee that climate change will be handled  by altering or relocating abstraction in space and by season. More monitoring bores may be needed, particularly where new routes for salinity exist because of deeper intrusion up estuaries. In dry seasons additional conductivity readings would be advisable at those sites which are marginal. Peck and Allison (1988) have demonstrated the usefulness of plotting fractional change in rainfall against recharge/ rainfall ratio in order to make contingency plans.

Tectonic or mining subsidence changes may initiate saline intrusion as readily as climate change and more rapidly in many circumstances. Mitigation measures are similar so lessons learned in one incident should assist with handling the next even if the exact cause or causes are unclear. The highest risk borehole sources remain those within 0.5 km of the coast where yields are high in fissured rock.

105

## Monitoring and research

It would be prudent for coastal authorities to monitor tidal embankment levels at least to the standard adopted for impounding reservoir banks; modern survey systems make this a more realistic request than the last generation would have expected.

This database needs to be matched by upper estuary cross-sections; the controlling ones for hydraulic purposes should be remeasured ideally each spring and autumn together with high and low tide levels. The latter can then be correlated with an estuary tide recorder, preferably of the latest intelligent logger type to facilitate rapid analysis.

Every estuary of note (in economic, community and ecologic terms) warrants a computer model of its flow regime and salinity status. Although a quick check suggests that perhaps eighteen have been carried out in Britain many of these concentrated on quality parameters such as dissolved oxygen rather than on velocity, depth and salinity. A comparable number have already been carried out in Malaysia and it seems surprising that in Britain the **Section 14 and 24 Surveys** were never followed up with comprehensive estuary simulation as a basis for the future.

Careful logging and analysis of pumped drainage flows is necessary to reveal whether, within the normal scatter of events, there is an underlying upward trend of energy required per hectare. A matching system is needed on gravity outfalls where the aim must be to discover whether discharge is changing seasonally and within the tidal cycle(s). The problem is more subtle in the gravity case and needs a parallel record of soil moisture and crop yields to be sure any significant change is emerging. Outfall measurements will need to be calibrated, probably by electromagnetic current meter, in order to obtain discharge coefficients for the real and very varied structures that exist; an intelligent level logger with a pair of level transducers

*Greenhouse effect and rising UK sea levels*

upstream and downstream will simplify what has previously been a tedious hydraulic analysis more often avoided than practised.

A baseline survey is needed of the 250 ppm chloride contour within all coastal aquifers. Initially this will need to be a fuzzy yes/no (fresh/salt) band until it can be made more precise. A reference sampling level at mean sea level is recommended but where levels are already below sea level a groundwater surface value could be accepted. Where the depth to saltwater is known this should be added to coastal groundwater maps (with the observation date) for future reference.

The Central Electricity Generating Board has probably monitored saline intrusion for longer than most other bodies because of their boiler make-up water needs. Examples, including computer modelling of the salinity regime, include Richborough power-station on the Kentish Stour and Drax power-station on the Yorkshire Ouse. By contrast the author believes that irrigation abstractors near tidal limits place reliance on water authority advice about river conditions. These are less obvious where irrigation is indirect as in the South Level, Cambridgeshire, or where there is tidal sluice underseepage from the sea 'contaminating' the source, so warranting seasonal monitoring.

Paradoxically the threat from the sea may be taken up as a positive challenge as with the Zuider Zee schemes in Holland. The need to control estuaries could lead to increased freshwater reaches and more reclaimed land. Presumably it was in large part due to the regular tidal threat to the Poulton - Lancaster road that the cost of reclamation by embanking of the Pilling salt marshes could be afforded in recent years.

The rapid growth of Geographic Information Systems should help the profession stay on top of the "Greenhouse" threat to its assets, keep the potential for change under review and help us persuade funding bodies to invest sooner rather than later.

NERC has a strong planned research programme in the climate change area and is co-ordinating that work between its Institutes through Mr Max Beran (Institute of Hydrology). Collaborative research with water agencies with specific concerns in this area would be welcomed in order to augment that sponsored by DoE and MAFF.

# 8

# POSSIBLE IMPACTS OF SEA-LEVEL RISE

# - A CASE STUDY FROM THE TEES ESTUARY,

# CLEVELAND COUNTY.

## I. SHENNAN and I. SPROXTON

### Background

There is much current interest regarding possible future sea level rise and how this may effect changes of the coastline and in the coastal lowlands of the United Kingdom. Since politicians and decision-makers aim to react efficiently in short-, medium- and long-term planning it may, at first, appear that the uncertainties over the magnitude of future changes in sea level are a major obstacle. This should not be the case as flexibility can be an essential part of current planning. In the meantime modelling and environmental monitoring can be refined in order to produce better predictions and a probability can then be assigned to individual sea level rise scenarios.

The review in Chapter 3 shows that there is a considerable level of uncertainty in the predictions of future sea level changes. This uncertainty is only important, however, in the context of the questions asked and should **not** be the basis for declining to ask questions and seek solutions. The context refers to the political, social and economic environments and the temporal and spatial scales of the investigation. Previous impact studies (eg Barth & Titus 1984, Carter 1987, Shennan 1987, Shennan & Tooley 1987) have noted a range of general options which include retreat, do nothing, advance or formulate structural responses to elevated water levels. Chapters 5, 6 and 9 in this book take a fresh look at the available options for the UK.

The extremes of the range of options, certainly for western developed nations (the practical responses for less developed nations must be considered against quite different benefits and costs), are those recommended or implemented within the USA and the Netherlands. In the Netherlands the baseline is that there are no areas to retreat to and the only options are to defend the land at great cost or even to create new land. Whereas in the USA loss of coastal land and planned retreat is now part of adopted policy in some states, (eg Maine and North Carolina; Titus 1987).

The starting point taken in this chapter is that no decision, at either of the extremes noted above, has been made at a national scale in the United Kingdom (see also Parker 1987) and that all options remain open.

On a local scale the Thames Barrier would appear to be a 'Dutch Solution' and the rapid erosion of unprotected cliffs in Holderness the other extreme. For each area local conditions must be evaluated and considered alongside national and global factors. Only when the precise questions, and the methods by which they are answered, are defined does the uncertainty of the sea level rise scenarios become an issue. It will also be shown that there are other equally important factors which cannot be predicted with any greater certainty.

For decisions to be made regarding the impacts of future sea level change and the method of coping with the perceived hazard some form of cost-benefit analysis is performed. This may be either formally as some sort of economic model or it may be within a non-monetary framework. There are three aspects to address (Jones 1989) : first the efficiency problem, or is it worth it ? Second, the equity concern, who are the winners and who are the losers ? Third, the effectiveness, does it do the job ? It becomes very difficult to answer these in the traditional economic framework since environmen-

*Possible impacts : Tees estuary*

tal factors cannot be addressed in simple financial terms. For the environmental aspects the 'willingness to pay' or 'bequeath value' approaches could be taken, though there are clear difficulties here. However, the broad framework for assessing impacts of sea level rise can be seen in Figure 8.1 (adapted from Jones 1989). In this context a case study of the Tees estuary can be considered.

## The Tees Estuary

The Tees estuary lies at the heart of the county of Cleveland (Figure 8.2), one of the most heavily industrialised and urbanised counties in the United Kingdom. The current population (1986) is 552,400. Out of a total area for the County of 6000 km$^2$, just over 100 km$^2$, around the middle and lower estuary lies below 10m OD, with 35 km$^2$ below 5m OD. The major concentrations of population are at Hartlepool, Billingham, Stockton-on-Tees, Middlesbrough and Redcar.

The industrial base of the county is changing. With traditional heavy industries such as ship building having declined, the main activities are manufacturing, fabrication yards servicing offshore industries, petro-chemicals and iron and steel production. Many of these facilities are close to the river, located on areas reclaimed from the estuary over the past 150 years. There are also major areas of redevelopment of derelict industrial land adjacent to the estuary.

Other significant land uses which must be considered are recreational facilities (eg golf courses, beaches) and nature conservation (marshes, dunes and intertidal flats).

The Tees estuary has been chosen as a case study for a number of reasons. Primarily it is a geographically circumscribed area containing a wide range of environments and land-use types. Thus various methods of identifying and assessing hazards and impacts can be evaluated without overwhelming data collection. Nevertheless one

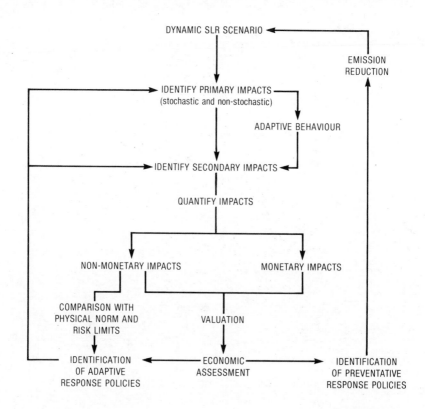

**FIGURE 8.1  A FRAMEWORK FOR ASSESSING IMPACTS OF SEA LEVEL RISE** (adapted from Jones, 1989)

*Possible impacts : Tees estuary*

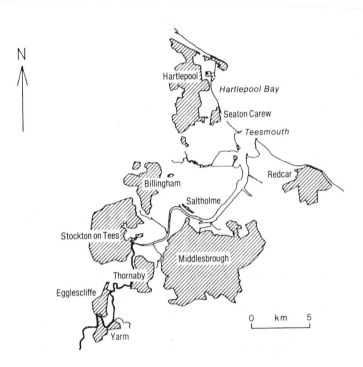

N

FIGURE 8.2 LOCATION MAP OF THE TEES ESTUARY

essential aspect has been to develop approaches which are not unique to one area but can be applied to other parts of the United Kingdom, and also at the national scale. As an illustration of this point, an early study of the Tees estuary (Shennan & Tooley 1987), used a geographic information system (GIS) to link readily available data on sea level rise scenarios, land altitudes and socio-economic variables. The advantages of the approach included accessibility of data, application at a range of scales, ease of data manipulation and management and a link between environmental factors and administrative units; while the major disadvantage was that the use of the administrative unit would overestimate the area likely to be affected. This can only be overcome by a significant increase in the resources given to data collection. Whether this increase is justified must depend on the questions asked in relation to a particular study. The important point is that all data collected and analyses performed should be compatible so that waste of resources is avoided. This emphasises the need for national guidelines which can then be integrated with local case studies.

The Tees case study presented in the following sections is a progression from the earlier study, though all the information from the latter is still usable. The initial approach has now been expanded to cover the east coast of England (Figure 8.3) and any of the analyses reported for individual estuaries (Shennan 1987a, Shennan & Tooley 1987) can be performed at this national scale.

## Risk - The Tees Estuary

### Perception of risk

Natural hazards only exist in relation to human activity, needs and aspirations and society copes by various forms of adaption or adjustment (Chapters 1 and 9, see also Whittow 1987). Coastal flooding has not, it would appear, been perceived as an important limitation on land use within the Tees estuary. Much of the recent in

*Possible impacts : Tees estuary*

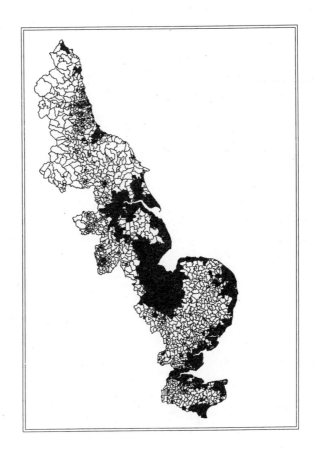

## FIGURE 8.3  WARDS IN EASTERN ENGLAND
## WITH MINIMUM GROUND ALTITUDES 5 m.
## OR LOWER

*Morphological, land use and census data are available for each ward to provide national scale information of the type discussed for earlier local studies (see Shennan, 1987a: Shennan and Tooley, 1989)*

*Greenhouse effect and rising UK sea levels*

dustrial development has taken place on land reclaimed from the
estuary and even a number of current redevelopment schemes make
no mention of sea-flood protection (see below). There is no record
of serious marine flooding in the area. The storm surges of 1953 and
1978 had a very limited affect on the Tees estuary in comparison with
other coastal lowlands around the Southern North Sea.

Flood hazard maps of the Cleveland coast and the Tees estuary were
produced by the Northumbrian Water Authority in 1972. The maps
form part of a series covering the north east coast from Berwick-
upon-Tweed to Skinningrove showing areas at risk from tidal and
tidally induced flooding. These areas are classified into four categories of risk on the basis of ground altitudes related to existing water
levels. The four categories cover the range 3.10 to 4.20m OD (D.
Archer, Northumbrian Water, pers. comm.). In addition to defining
the areas within each class the maps draw attention to significant
point locations such as factories and low lying stretches of main
roads. The maps have two important benefits: the areas shown are
defined on the basis of detailed levelling; and they provide an
accurate assessment of potential flood extent at the time of survey.
However, the maps and the material used in their production suffer
from a number of limitations: no account is taken of intervening
defences or increased ground elevations and therefore likelihood of
flooding; the information needs regular updating to take into account
of land use changes; the maps rely on detailed levelling which is time
consuming and therefore expensive to produce; being related to
existing water levels no account is taken of potential future levels;
they are only lines on maps and therefore indicate only where
problems may occur, so they need to be linked to information on
what will be affected by sea level rise, ground water rise and
associated flooding.

The perception of risk must also be considered with respect to the
socio-economic environment of the area. From a total population of
552,400 (1986) the labour force of Cleveland was c.260,000 but only

c.210,000 available jobs. The 'job gap' is projected to show only a small decline by AD 2000 due to a decrease in the labour force, an ageing population, and an increase in service jobs (Cleveland County Council Structure Plan data). Therefore against a background of the loss of jobs from traditional industries such as ship building and iron and steel production, developments over the past 30 years in what now appear to be risk areas can be justified. Equally, it needs to be a very carefully argued and costed case to impose restrictions based on increased flood risk on any new developments which will provide important employment and growth to the local economy.

### Definition of the environmental hazard

There are 4 major environmental factors to be evaluated namely the crustal, wave, tidal, and sedimentary environments.

#### Crustal environment.

Shennan (1989a) has estimated that late Holocene crustal deformation in Great Britain is most probably within the range of +2.0 to -2.0mm/yr, with maximum uplift in central-western Scotland and maximum subsidence in East Anglia and the Thames estuary. The Tees estuary, from a limited data base, shows a rate close to zero. This would suggest that no correction to the global figure for any particular sea level rise scenario is required due to local crustal factors. It should be noted, however, that a significant contribution to the volume of water in the oceans from melting of the Greenland and/or Antarctic icesheet(s) could modify the global mean value (Clark & Primus 1987) due to gravitational effects (Chapter 3).

#### Wave environment.

The north east coast of England is currently exposed to wind generated storm waves and the threat of future sea level rise is both the gradual inundation of coastal areas and the effects of storm surges, which for any particular design level the return period will decrease as sea level rises (see Rossiter 1962 and the discussion below).

## Tidal environment.

The Tees estuary is a macro-tidal environment, current spring tide range is 4.60m and extreme predicted range 7.24m, and the prediction of a rise in mean sea level of perhaps less than 1m in 100 years could be perceived by some individuals as insignificant,(ie daily changes appear to be larger than the so-called hazard). In addition there is an increase of 0.20m of mean high water of spring tides upstream within the tidal part of the estuary, and high water levels will also be affected by freshwater discharge from the Tees catchment. The level of the Tees is subject to very rapid variations due to periods of intense rainfall in the upland catchment (House & Fullerton 1960) although some regulation is now provided using reservoir storage.

## Sedimentary environment

Coastline changes are not simply a response to changes in sea level but are greatly influenced by other factors including the nature of the sedimentary environment, particularly the spatial and temporal patterns of erosion and deposition. These can vary over a wide range of scales and it is frequently the case that even where a series of direct observations have been made they are likely to be spatially and temporally restricted. Hydraulics Research (1986) has shown that there is a major longshore drift component from the north, where the cliffs of Magnesian Limestone, and the dumping of colliery waste, provide clastic material for the beaches and dunes at North Sands, Hartlepool Bay and the North and South Gares (the two artificial breakwaters at the mouth of the Tees). There is a smaller, localised, northwest drift from Coatham Sands. Even within the major zone of sand deposition there are localised areas of erosion of current sea defences, eg at

*Possible impacts : Tees estuary*

Hartlepool Headland and Seaton Carew. Under these conditions where there is a significant longshore component relatively simple models, such as the Bruun Rule, may provide poor results (see Orford 1987). The relative importance of the longshore component will also vary according to the rate of sea level change.

The present sedimentary environment must be viewed with respect to the present coastal configuration and known sediment sources, but a wider perspective can be obtained from a study of coastal geomorphology and sedimentary sequences. In a quite different environment, Suez City, Cooke (1988) was able to use a field survey of the geomorphology of the area to provide the data necessary for the preparation of a relative flood hazard map even though no runoff data were available. Similarly analysis of estuarine sediment sequences can show the magnitude of past coastline changes, related to both palaeogeography and rate of sea level change (Shennan 1987b, 1989b). The response of coastal sedimentary systems to varying rates of sea level change are likely to be non-linear (Orford 1987) and characterised by time lags (eg Allen 1990). In the Tees estuary marine sediments have accumulated since c. 9700 BP (Shennan 1983, Tooley unpublished data) but with a number of periods of coastline advance and retreat. In contrast Hartlepool Bay has changed from an area of low energy clastic and organic sediment accumulation around 6000 BP (Tooley 1978 and unpublished data) to the present high energy eroding sandy coast. This has resulted from a combination of sea level change and changes in coastal geomorphology. Where possible the conditions under which both gradual and catastrophic changes can take place should be identified  even if the precise method of modelling them is not available. Therefore the method of impact assessment must be able to use new geomorphological analyses as they become available.

The most recent changes in sediment accumulation within the estuary have been due to the construction of the breakwaters (the South Gare 1863 - 1888 and North Gare 1882 - 1891) at the mouth of the river using 4 million tonnes of industrial slag, and reclamation of intertidal flats for industrial development from the 1860s to the 1970s.

The wave, tidal and sedimentary factors may well change in the future along with sea level rise and rainfall patterns, the latter influencing river discharge rates. Management decisions, such as dredging and drainage basin control, will also be important. The uncertainties of the proportional effects of each of these may well be as large as those for sea level change.

### Risk definition

Once an environmental hazard has been perceived the risk needs to be assessed. This can be done in a number of ways. Frequently for the definition of flood defence standards, or other types of coastal engineering structures, the return period of extreme water levels are calculated.

An additional allowance for wave height and freeboard may be added. Data have been supplied by Northumbrian Water from which the return periods for water levels within the estuary, ie with no significant waves, have been calculated (Table 8.1).

The recommended minimum defence standard for frontages within the estuary is 4.65m OD, which is within the envelope of the 1:1000 to 1:10000 year return period at Tees Dock and is in accord with the standards employed elsewhere, such as in the Netherlands (Knoester 1984). A 0.35m sea level rise by the year 2050, a value within the mid-range of recent estimates, would reduce the return period at any level by a factor of approximately 10.

A second approach is to define the areas at risk. This involves a consideration of both a much larger area than the immediate coastal frontage and a range of environmental hazards. For the Tees estuary

*Possible impacts : Tees estuary*

## TABLE 8.1

## RETURN PERIODS FOR THE TEES AND
## MIDDLESBROUGH DOCKS WITHIN THE TEES ESTUARY

*The frequencies were calculated using incomplete records from Tees Dock for the period 1921-1983, and estimates for Middlesbrough Dock were then made. Data and calculations by Northumbrian Water for 1:10 and 1:100yr at Tees Dock. A linear extrapolation was used for the other figures but must be treated with caution.*

| Return period | Tees Dock metres OD | Middlesbrough Dock metres OD |
|---|---|---|
| 1:10yr | c. 3.65 | c. 3.82 |
| 1:100yr | c. 4.00 | c. 4.25 |
| 1:1000yr | c. 4.35 | c. 4.68 |
| 1:10000yr | c. 4.70 | c. 5.11 |

there are two major groups of hazards, and several of less consequence. The first is the potential impact of sea level rise due to long term inundation and seepage within the groundwater table, and the second is coastal erosion, associated with normal coastal processes, an adjustment to changing sea level, and also the effects of single, high energy events.

Two scenarios of sea level rise are shown in Figure 8.4. The basic predictions are the low and mid-range low scenarios of Hoffman (1984), which provide an envelope for a range of recent predictions (revised predictions quoted by Titus 1987 as Hoffman et al 1985 give

*Greenhouse effect and rising UK sea levels*

similar figures for the period to AD 2050 but with a rapid rise, over 3m, in the following 50 years for the high estimate. This acceleration is much greater than other estimates and is not considered further here). Each graph shows four parallel lines, each representing a method from which the level of risk can be defined. The bottom line has an origin at the level of current highest astronomical tides (HAT) (3.25m OD), the next line starts at the highest recorded water level (4.01m OD, in 1953), the third at MHWST plus 1.60m, where 1.60m is the computed surge with a 50 year return period (Flather 1987) and the highest line is for HAT plus 2.19m. In the 1953 storm surge the highest recorded water level of 4.01m OD did not coincide with high tide, therefore damage was limited, but the surge component was 2.19m (calculated from Rossiter 1954). Thus the top line represents the extreme combination of a coincidence of a large storm surge at maximum predicted water level. The probability of this occurring is very small but the range of risks should be identified.

For the first stage analysis of areas at risk and the potential impacts the 5m OD level has been used, for a number of reasons. Firstly it is a good estimate for various levels of risk by 2050, within a reasonable margin of error, and secondly it is a very practical option, since the Ordnance Survey contours are at 0m and 5m. If an alternative level was defined interpolation of ground altitudes from Ordnance Survey digital data would be required to identify areas at risk (This is part of a CEC sponsored research project at Durham University).

Detailed ground levelling (as applied already by Northumbrian Water in 1972) or photogrammetric survey are other possible methods. Therefore the 5m contour is a practical and meaningful base for assessing impacts for this area.

*Possible impacts : Tees estuary*

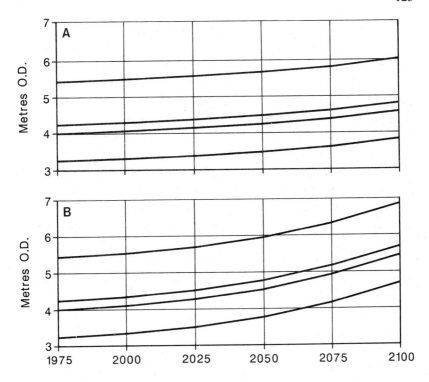

## FIGURE 8.4 TWO SCENARIOS OF
## SEA LEVEL CHANGE

A) The low scenario of Hoffman (1984) adapted to local tidal conditions in the Tees estuary to show the rise of various levels of risk (see text), related to ground altitudes, to AD 2100.

B) The mid-range low scenario of Hoffman (1984) adapted as in A.


### Impacts and Possible Responses

Within a relatively small area the Tees estuary and its environs are a microcosm of virtually all of the impacts likely to affect the United Kingdom.

### Coastal erosion and deposition

In the absence of any long term quantitative assessment based on a series of past records, future changes may have to be based on an extrapolation of recent trends, although these are influenced by human activities. Undercutting of sea walls, at Hartlepool Headland and Seaton Carew, and erosion of sand dunes north of Hartlepool (behind which is a large industrial plant) are indicative of current coastal changes. Simple application of the Bruun Rule must be viewed with caution due to the significant longshore contribution (Orford 1987) of sediment from the north. Any rise in sea level would increase erosion of the cliffs to the north and there may be an increase in sediment input to the beaches around the Tees. The sediment balance may already be out of equilibrium due to the reduction in the dumping of colliery spoil on the beach to the north. This has had a visible effect on local bays and headlands there but it is not known whether any effect has been transmitted south to the Tees and Hartlepool area. Various methods of prediction are required, such as those reviewed by Orford (1987) and Leatherman (1984), before any further statements can be made.

One further area where any increase in erosion will have major effects is at the mouth of the Tees, where sand dunes have developed as a response to the building of the breakwaters.

### Loss of wetlands and other habitats.

There are four designated Sites of Special Scientific Interest (Figure 8.5) which meet the criteria both for designation under the terms of E.C. Directive 79/409/EEC on the conservation of wild birds and for inclusion on the list of Wetlands of International Importance under the Ramsar Convention. The sites, in total 1100 ha., include dune, intertidal flat and salt marsh habitats which support a diverse flora and fauna in addition to large colonies of breeding and migrating birds (Ratcliffe 1977). These areas of international significance have

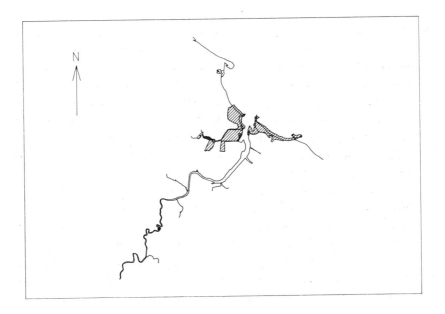

**FIGURE 8.5 SITES OF SPECIAL SCIENTIFIC
INTEREST IN THE TEES ESTUARY**

already suffered major reductions in size due to land reclamation. They are particularly vulnerable to disturbance in the event of sea level rise because embankments and installations to the landward prevent and significant migration landwards as water levels rise (Sproxton 1989). If the habitats are to be preserved the cost of tidal management schemes, as part of a broader sea defence programme, must be assessed against the non-monetary benefits.

**Urban residential areas at risk.**

The main residential areas are above 5m OD, Figure 8.6, with approximately 600 houses in areas (total 1.2 km$^2$) below the 5m contour, which includes the high risk category areas defined by the water authority in 1973. If the 5m contour were to be adopted as a policy decision to define areas at risk and impose any land use restrictions there would be far reaching consequences which could affect property insurance rates and resale value for example, which could lead to a blight on the areas involved and subsequent social factors such as stress. These consequences need to be carefully considered, before any precise designations are made. There may be legal implications.

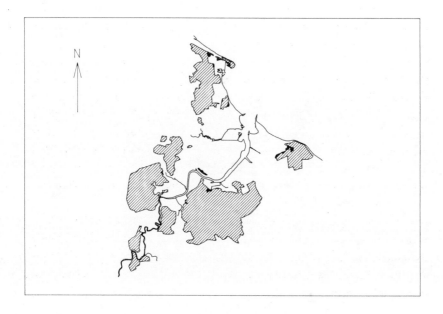

**FIGURE 8.6 URBAN AREAS IN CLEVELAND**
(areas below 5m OD in heavier shading)

*Possible impacts : Tees estuary*

In an assessment of the impact of sea level rise on urban areas one of the advantages of the GIS approach can be appreciated. Ordnance Survey digital map data, integrated with census data, can be used to attribute information to individual house properties, such as type, average number of occupants, flood damage information (eg Penning--Rowsell 1988). These data can be used in any cost-benefit analysis. In addition land use changes can be easily incorporated at the planning stage whereas areas delineated on large scale paper maps quickly become out of date.

**Industrial areas at risk**

There are at least 10 major industrial complexes located within the area identified as being at risk (Figure 8.7). For these complexes the impact of sea level rise needs to be considered in terms of the potential for damage to plant and equipment, raw materials and finished products as well as possible disruption of production. The general economic implications can be illustrated with reference to one plant which is already dependent on sea defence embankments since it is in part on land at 3m OD. The capital value of the plant is estimated at £ 100 million, with an annual production of £ 75 million and a workforce of 600. In addition there would be the environmental risk of the potential release of toxic substances during a flooding event.

Work is currently underway to calculate the relevant economic variables for all the industrial activities in the flood risk areas so that any future investment in sea defences, or alternatives, can be assessed in financial terms.

**FIGURE 8.7 INDUSTRIAL AREAS IN CLEVELAND**
(areas below 5m. OD in heavier shading)

## Transport networks

Although the pattern of reclamation of intertidal areas in the estuary during the last 40 years resulted in the elevation of the land surface to above 5m, the road network serving the industrial complexes located in these areas includes significant sections which cross low-lying ground at risk from inundation (Figure 8.8). Any flooding of these sections of roads, including two 'A Class' roads, would curtail access to and egress from the industrial complexes, and hinder emergency services in the event of a major incident triggered by high water levels.

*Possible impacts : Tees estuary*

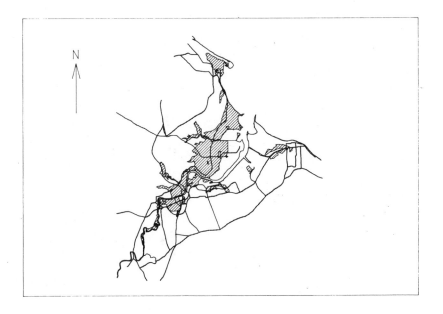

**FIGURE 8.8 TRANSPORT NETWORK AND
AREAS BELOW 5 m. OD**

### Landfills and waste disposal sites

There are at least 30 landfill sites in risk areas. For this category the 10m contour is used since the altitude of the base of each landfill is not known. Any changes in ground water pressure and seepage rates within or around landfill sites due to sea level rise will be important because of the potential for the reactivation and mobilisation of toxins and their transmission to the environment. A detailed assessment should be made for each site indicating the potential for effects of groundwater changes and direct inundation.

## Agriculture

Around Saltholme there is just over 1000ha given over to arable cultivation and grazing, with c.600 ha below 5m OD. The land is valued at c. £ 5000 per hectare and annual production is currently c. £ 500 per hectare. An economic and ecological assessment of the area must include consideration of the consequences of changes in the level of local groundwater on the choice of agriculture practised and the costs and benefits of artificial drainage and sea defence investments.

## New developments

There are currently three major new projects, at different stages of development, each on land which is in part below 5m OD.

At the Stockton racecourse site an £ 80 million retail and recreation complex is under construction. The river embankments are being improved but details of defence altitudes and land drainage specifications are not known at present.

At Hartlepool, a marina complex, including 150 housing units, with a capital value estimate at £ 150 million is in the early stages of development as part of the now derelict dock area.

The proposed barrage across the Tees, and the associated development of a riverside park consisting of industrial, retail, office and housing units (total investment around £ 220 million), is delayed at present due to the failure of the associated Private Member's Bill in the last Parliamentary session of 1989. The barrage part of the project consisted of a moveable weir which would impound water upstream so that intertidal sediments would not be exposed in the river channel, thus improving the quality of the riverside environment. The impounding level is 2.65m OD and the maximum level of the weir is 4.5m OD. The envisaged flood control role would be to lower the level of the weir during periods of high river discharge. As presently envisaged the role of the proposed barrage does not include a marine flooding protection function except to prevent the transfer of polluted saline waters into the impounded water body upstream. If this aspect was to be added to the specification some redesign would apparently be required, if only to reach the current minimum defence level defined by Northumbrian Water (4.65m OD) with a higher level required if future sea level rise is taken into account.

## Conclusions

Within the relatively small area of the Cleveland coast and Tees Estuary there is a wide range of possible impacts of future sea level rise that could be used as the basis for national scale planning. At present the areas at risk and the type of risk can be defined. However, not all the required information is in the correct form for assimilation and analysis. There are also significant gaps in the environmental and economic data base, such as detailed topographic information, current rates of sediment transfer, property values, capital and recurrent commercial and industrial costs. These are all required if impacts of sea level rise are to be evaluated with various analyses of the environmental and economic costs and benefits.

The aim of this case study is to expound a method by which these various analyses can be carried out repetitively, either for the same area at different times as economic and environmental baseline conditions change, or for different areas, and at different scales. This is not intended to be a completed, one-off case study. The case study is incomplete due to the necessary delay in transferring the available data to digital form, and identifying the gaps in the data base. The GIS method has been used to delineate a set of land use risk maps, and the economic modelling is under development using the database functions and compatible packages. The next stage, currently in progress, is to develop the research using the digital data held by

Cleveland County Council, and provide a method of impact evaluation that can contribute directly to established decision-making structures.

The GIS approach advocated here is applicable at a range of integrated scales but the problems of data availability, existence or in an incompatible form, and data quality, especially for physical processes, are not unique to this approach. As data requirements are defined and solved so the prediction of impacts improves. The flexibility of the approach adopted here will ensure an efficient re-evaluation of environmental and economic scenarios as the parameters are changed in light of the new information.

There are problems of perception associated with the definition of any level to define areas at risk. The 5m level is valuable for this area but is not a universal figure for the United Kingdom due to the range of tide and surge components. For example for at Boston Grand Sluice, in the Fenland, extreme high water of spring tides is 4.60m OD, the highest recorded water level is 5.63m OD and the minimum defence standard for the western shore of the Wash, set by Anglian Water is currently 6.0m OD (data supplied by Anglian Water). With most of the Fenland below the level of extreme high tides a map of areas at risk for any reasonable sea level rise scenario would be little different in many respects to a map showing the areas already requiring protection. Identification of an area at risk is open to misinterpretation if selectively reported, as revealed by the recent use of the ARK map and report (ARK 1989) by national newspapers. It is the responsibility of scientists to be cautious in their use of such information and to avoid being alarmist, or avoid being interpreted as alarmist. The inaccurate use of publications, lack of citation, and an uncritical selection and extrapolation of single extreme figures, when a range had been stated, within the scientific literature (eg Boorman et al 1989) is misleading, indefensible and could devalue the work of other scientists contributing to sea level research.

## Acknowledgements

Numerous people at Northumbrian Water and Cleveland County Council have provided valuable information, but the views expressed here are those of the authors and reflect no endorsement by NW or CCC. Michael Tooley made many valuable comments on a draft of the paper. The research was supported by The Commission of the European Community (contract EVAC 0049 to I Shennan and M J Tooley) and the University of Durham (Research Leave granted to I Shennan).

# 9

# POLICY, PLANNING AND ENGINEERING REACTIONS

# TO SEA LEVEL RISE

## J. C. DOORNKAMP

Realistically speaking it seems unlikely that anything will be done by the global community to prevent climatic forcing by greenhouse gases. Indeed, the climatic reaction to past inputs of greenhouse gases is still awaited. Even total emission control now would have little impact on greenhouse effects for several decades and little can be achieved in terms of mitigation during the next century (Barth and Titus, 1984). Nations are unlikely to accept the considerable industrial, economic and competitive disadvantages that would be associated with "going it alone" in terms of emission controls. Despite considerable lip-service there still seems to be insufficient international motivation to tackle the problem (Seidel and Keyes, 1983; Von Moltke, 1989). The oceanic and sea level response will be a global rise, according to Van Der Veen (1989), of the order of 22-66 cms by 2085 at a rate 4-6 times greater than that measured over the last century.

Given that all of this is the case, what policy, planning and engineering reactions are appropriate ?
Two of the most important questions concerning sea level rise are:

- by how much ?
- how soon ?

Other chapters in this book have indicated that sea level rise around the UK coast will probably be of the order of 20 cms by the year 2030, though a rise of as little as 5 cms and as much as 40 cms is predicted by some models.

If we couple to this the concept of increased storminess and the consequent potential for storm damage, there is a sufficient need to think **now** about the actions that should be taken to deal with the predicted conditions.

Chapters 5-8 have dealt with the potential effects on specific parts of the UK coastline. This chapter is more concerned to identify the range of policy planning and engineering options, and their relative costs, that are available to those who manage the shoreline.

## General Strategies for Coping with Natural Hazards

Studies of other natural perils (e.g. floods, earthquakes and landslides) have led to the formulation of a set of available alternatives. These form a logical suite of options that could be considered by every coastal local authority in the Uk when reviewing their own management reaction to the rising sea level/increased storminess scenario.

These alternative reactions are set out in Figure 9.1. They include the two alternatives:

    A.  do nothing
    B.  take action.

### Doing nothing

- This may happen through a lack of awareness and the affected group are over-taken by the event, in which case they may be forced into a rapid defensive action (see below).

- This may happen as a conscious decision (political, economic or both), in which case, should the peril arise the group is also forced into rapid defensive action (see below).

*Policy, planning and engineering reactions*

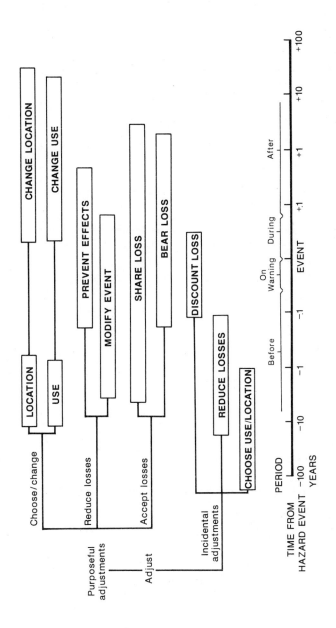

**FIGURE 9.1 ALTERNATIVE STRATEGIES FOR COPING WITH NATURAL HAZARDS.**

(From Burton, Kates, and White, 1978)

*Greenhouse effect and rising UK sea levels*

Doing nothing is the most common response to natural perils which are not a frequent experience of a community. In the case of river flooding on flood plains, for example, the concept of policy-by-crisis was well defined by Hart (1957). Increased awareness, experience, and scientific understanding since that time has, in many cases decreased the emphasis on "crisis" and increased that on "management policy". Ultimately crisis management is the most costly form of management in terms of both money and personal grief. It involves bearing the losses that arise, or at best sharing those costs (e.g. through insurance policies or national disaster funds). The instinctive reaction is to then carry out remedial measures (which if carried out sooner would have been preventative measures).

Studies of coastal management problems (eg. Mitchell, 1974) have shown that different human and social reactions will manifest themselves according to the size of the population of the affected area, the economic activity within the area, and the prevailing social conditions.

### Taking action

1. How ?

This may be by undertaking changes and making adjustments involving engineering works (e.g. increasing coastal defences), or it may be through a planning strategy (e.g. by adopting a three-fold zonation of: prohibitive zone, restrictive zone, and a warning zone). An interesting comparison may be made with quoted examples of a range of managerial choices used in relation to large-scale flooding in North America (Table 9.1).

In practice not all of these have the effect of reducing the risk of damage. The facilitation of insurance and the provision of income tax relief help to reduce the costs to individuals, they do not amount to planning control.

*Policy, planning and engineering reactions*

## TABLE 9.1

## MANAGERIAL CHOICES IN THE CASE OF LARGE-SCALE FLOODS IN THE USA.

ACTION

| | |
|---|---|
| Pre-emptive | Transfer of floodable land to public ownership. |
| Mandatory | Introduction of appropriate local building codes |
| Influencing | Subsidized (storm and) flood damage insurance |
| Informative | Information provided to increase local awareness |
| Incidental | Income tax deductions for flood losses |

For many people the ecologically most sound approach is to adopt a combined engineering and planning strategy.

Either way it involves policy decisions based on the need to reach declared objectives concerning the management of the coast (see Chapter 1).

Such policy decisions can only be taken in an atmosphere of awareness amongst the policy-makers, in this case usually lay-persons locally elected and guided by officers not all of whom may be "in the know".

*Greenhouse effect and rising UK sea levels*

2. When ?

This may be now, in the early days of global warming/rising sea level awareness, when the basic science of prediction is still filled with some self-doubt about the basic questions concerning "how fast?" and "by how much?".

Alternatively it may be in the medium term, when more tangible evidence has emerged, when some damage has been experienced in the most vulnerable parts of the world (or UK).

It may be some time later when that particular portion of coast has been directly affected - and a rapid defensive reaction may set in.

This last alternative comes close to crisis management as a reaction mode, and does not allow either good judgement or the most cost-effective solution.

3. How much ?

The range of possible reactions vary from a full engineering scheme to meet the most extreme conditions predicted, to a bit-at-a-time approach.

As a general policy engineering schemes (and indeed planning schemes for that matter) are best formulated as a comprehensive integrated plan which, though carried out on a stage-by-stage basis, form one adequate system when completed.

**The Management Problems**

Within the UK context of coastal management the agencies for an effective response to issues such as rising sea level are somewhat elusive. Historically there has been a mis-match between dynamic

*Policy, planning and engineering reactions*

coastal systems (e.g. sites of erosion, sites of deposition and the processes of sediment transport between then). To some extent this has been over-come by the creation (even if on an informal basis) of groups of coastal authorities such as SCOPAC. Ultimately the protection of any one part of lowland coastal Britain also depends on adequate protection being afforded to the rest of that part of lowland coastal Britain.

If there is a concerted realization that there is a looming coastal protection problem this may well lead to further concerted action invloving pressure on Central Government to fund any necessary works. This may be justified in view of the fact that rising sea levels around the whole of Britain is a national as well as a local problem.

There is, however, an even more deep-seated issue. Experience world-wide has shown that industrial societies, such as that in Britain, much more readily adopt a confrontational approach to natural perils than is the case with a less industrialised society. We elect to engineer a protection against the forces of nature rather than to adopt modifications in our behaviour which allow for changes in the natural world.

The alternative, of dealing with the problem through a planning/policy option which seeks changes in land use in order to adapt to the consequences of rising sea levels, is always available. Examples of such reactions exist. The capital of Belize was moved inland following a hurricane disaster. In the case of Venice and Tokyo policy decisions were made to cease water-abstraction from beneath these cities so as to decrease the threat of subsidence and consequent flooding. These decisions cost money, but the communities concerned saw adaptation to their changing environment as a better answer than hard engineering.

In the UK case the immediate concern, using a planning strategy, will be to consider land-use alternatives for those lowland areas likely to be affected by inundation (see Chapter 7). But, other areas and types

## TABLE 9.2 RELATIVE COSTS OF ACTIONS TAKEN
## AT DIFFERENT TIMES

| Option | Short-Term Costs | Medium-Term Costs | Long-Term Costs | Residual Costs | Total Costs |
|---|---|---|---|---|---|
| No change in policies now (late reaction): | 1 | 2 | 6 | 6 | 15 |
| Medium-term adaptation: | 2 | 3 | 4 | 3 | 12 |
| Immediate adaptation: | 4 | 0 | 0 | 0 | 4 |

*The total cost of any one option is the sum of costs along the row. (e.g. No change in policy means that some coastal protection work will continue, in the short term. As sea level/storminess conditions begin to change medium term costs will be higher, and if a major incursion of the sea takes place (and/or excessive erosion occurs) rapid defensive reactions may set in, at a much higher cost, with a residual cost in terms of damage already experienced, still to be met. Immediate adaptation, through planning and/or engineering reactions, while involving financial outlay now, may yield much lower total costs. However, this approach could also lead to complacency!).*

*Policy, planning and engineering reactions*

of sites will also be affected (see Chapter 5, 7 and 8). If increased wave-height leads to further coastal erosion there may be an acceleration of cliff-top retreat (e.g. in the soft-rock cliffs of eastern and southern England). Such areas will also require consideration. Is it to be more sea defences or the introduction of zones (or corridors) of no development within a specified distance of the present cliff top ? Studies of human responses to coastal erosion such as that by Mitchell (1974) provide a valuable insight to the social reactions that are involved.

**Comparative costs**

While it is impossible to provide absolute costs of each of the strategy options defined above, past experience has again shown what relative costs may be. Table 9.2 sets these out.
Alternative reactions

Studies of the adjustments made by people to flooding provide a useful set of guidelines to the alternatives available for dealing with problems consequent upon a rise in sea level.

By analogy with reactions to river flooding, and by comparisons with studies of reactions to coastal flooding, the alternative adjustments likely to be considered under a rising sea level scenario are (see also Chapter 1) :

1.   Modifying the behaviour of the sea:
          - Flood protection
          - Sea-walls
          - Embankments
          - Beach nourishment
          - Breakwaters
          - Land elevation and fill

2. Modify the susceptibility to damage:
   - Land-use regulation and changes
   - Zoning ordinances
   - Changes in Building codes
   - Urban renewal beyond the threatened areas
   - Compulsory purchase of vulnerable sites/properties
   - Subsidised relocation
   - Local additional defensive works (including land elevation and fill)

3. Modify the loss burden
   - Introduce appropriate insurance schemes
   - Create disaster relief funds
   - Prepare emergency measures, including evacuation plans
   - Establish emergency communication lines.

4. Do nothing
   - Bear the full cost of the loss

These alternative reactions clearly include elements of planning and engineering, and require a co-ordinated policy approach. However, an appropriate approach cannot be defined until the scale, nature and timing of the likely impacts of a rising sea level have been evaluated for the coastline in question. Such an evaluation could be carried out using guidelines available for Environmental (Impact) Assessments (EIAs) (see Canter, 1977; Marsh, 1978; Heer and Hagerty, 1977). These would allow an objective assessment to be made of the social, economic, and physical aspects of the problem in the particular context in which a local (or indeed national) administration finds itself in the context of this issue. It would provide one of the very few examples of an EIA being carried out on a physical ("natural") process rather than on a human action.

*Policy, planning and engineering reactions*

The chapters of this book have sought to identify and clarify the physical principles of the greenhouse effect and the likely reactions in terms of sea level rise around the shores of the UK. It has been necessary to place this in a global context for it is a global issue. There are signs that there will need to be a concerted effort by the global community to deal with the more dramatic of the consequences arising out of this whole problem (see the discussion in Hall and Doornkamp, 1989). The world's attention will be focused, for example, on the threat to areas such as the Ganges delta where sea level rise is likely to threaten millions of lives and millions of hectares of valuable agricultural land. In Britain a certain self-sufficiency may be assumed by the global community, though a concerted attempt at self-support by the whole of the European Community may not be out of the question. Local Government reactions to the problem will probably, therefore, have to be set within a national policy if and when this is forthcoming. The likelihood may be that shared responsibility will develop with major defenses (or other form of adjustment !) carried out under a national scheme and more local adaptations being the responsibility of the local authority.

Whatever the outcome in terms of responsibilities, this book has shown that administrators and coastal managers are faced with many choices over the next decade. The main choice concerns the timing of their reactions to the issue of rising sea levels, not as they perceive it but as it really is. Such reactions as are adopted need to be formulated within a clearly defined policy. Such policy will probably need to accept a blend of planning and engineering reactions as is most socially, economically and politically acceptable within the local area.

# 10

# DEPARTMENT OF THE

# ENVIRONMENT RESPONSE

## A.J.APLING

As the preceding chapters have shown, the greenhouse effect arises out of the combined effects of many individual and often small contributions. The UK contribution to the global total of carbon dioxide emissions, for example, is only 3 %.

There is no unilateral action which an individual country can take in order to solve the problem. An international approach is needed, on a global scale, whereby reductions in the emission of greenhouse gases is made wherever possible, and then to assess their cumulative effect.

The Intergovernmental Panel on Climate Change (IPCC) which has been set up jointly by the United Nations Environmental Programme (UNEP) and the World Meteorological Organization (WMO) has emerged as the key international focus for scientific and policy considerations about climate change.

The IPCC was established in November 1988 with a brief to provide an interim report in time for discussion at the World Climate Conference in November 1990. Working groups have already been set up to report on:

- A scientific assessment of the greenhouse effect
- The potential impacts arising out of global warming
- The response strategies which should be considered.

The Science group is chaired by Dr J Houghton, Director General of the UK Meteorological Office and is supported by a special team and facilities funded by the UK Departments of Environment and Energy. It will be looking at a wide range of climatic factors including:

- The science behind global warming predictions
- A comparative study of general circulation models (GCMs)
- A study of environmental feedback effects and interactions
- An investigation of other predictive techniques.

The main aim of all of this work is to try to narrow as far as possible the limits of uncertainty, outlined in earlier chapters, that still exist, concerning predictions of climate change.

The impacts group is being chaired by the USSR. It will be looking at possible impacts of the greenhouse effect on:

- Agriculture and other managed ecosystems
- Natural ecosystems
- Centres of habitation
- Social infrastructure.

Contributions to the deliberations of this group will be provided from the UK by Professor Parry of Birmingham University, supported by a small team funded by the DOE.

The response strategies group is to be chaired by the USA and would be looking at the full range of possible strategies that might be considered in response to the greenhouse effect. These will include a review of :

- Avoidance by the control of emissions
- Adaptive responses.
- Financial, Economic and Legal measures

The UK Department of Energy is making a contribution to the work of this group in the area of emission control options in the Energy

*Department of the Environment response*

and Industry sector.

The UK has been in the forefront of international efforts to recognise and develop an international response to the challenge of the greenhouse effect. The Government has supported the idea of a framework "Umbrella Convention" with the subsequent development of a range of binding Protocols to cover individual aspects of control.

The final IPCC report will be a major milestone in establishing the scientific, technical and policy issues of climate change. It will be discussed at Ministerial level at the Second World Climate Conference in November 1990.

Whilst reaching agreement on scientific and technical matters is a start, very difficult issues remain concerning policies for effective reduction of emissions; not least because of the profound impacts that large emission control policies would have on the present way of life in the developed world and the impact it may have on the aspirations and expectations of those in the less developed countries.

# BIBLIOGRAPHY AND REFERENCES

Allen, J. R. L., 1990 Constraints on measurement of sea level movements from salt-marsh accretion rates. *Jl. Geol. Soc., London,* **147,** 5-7

ARK 1989 Press statement to accompany the ARK *"After the Flood"* map of the United Kingdom in the year 2050.

Barnett, T. P., 1984 The estimation of "global" sea level change: a problem of uniqueness. *Journal of Geophys. Research,* **89,** 7980-7988.

Barth, M. C. and J. G. Titus (eds.), 1984 *The Greenhouse Effect and Sea Level Rise: a Challenge for this Generation,* (Van Norstrand Reinhold Company, New York).

Beran, M. A. and N. W. Arnell, 1989 *Effect of Climatic Change on Quantitative Aspects of United Kingdom Water Resources,* Report of Dept. of Environment (Water Directorate) 93pp.

Berger, A., 1980 The Milankovitch theory of paleoclimates a modern review. *Vistas in Astronomy,* **24,** 103-122

Boorman, L. A., Goss-Custard, J. D., and S. McGroty, 1989, *Climate Change, Rising Sea Level and the British Coast,* ITE Research Publication **No. 1,** (HMSO, London)

Bruun P., 1954 *Coastal Erosion and Development of Beach Profiles,* Technical Memo No 44 Washington (Beach Erosion Board).

Bruun P., 1988, The Bruun Rule of erosion by sea-level rise: a discussion of large scale two- and three-dimensional usages, *Journal of Coastal Res.,* **4 (4)** 627-648.

Budd, W. F., 1988 The expected sea-level rise from climatic warming in the Antarctic. In: G. I. Pearman (ed.), *Greenhouse, Planning for Climatic Change.* (Brill for CSIRO, Australia), 74-82.

Budyko, M. I., 1982 *The Earth's Climate: Past and Future,* (Academic Press, Orlando, Florida) 307 pp.

Burton, I., Kates, R. W. and R. Snead, 1969 *The Human Ecology of Coastal Flood Hazard in Megalopolis,* Research Paper **No. 115** (Dept. of Geography, University of Chicago) 196 pp.

Burton, I., Kates, R. W. and G. F. White, 1968 *The Human Ecology of Extreme Geophysical Events,* Natural Hazard Research

152

Working Paper **No. 1**, (Dept. of Geography, University of Toronto)

Burton, I., Kates, R. W. and G. F. White, 1978 *The Environment as Hazard*, (Oxford University Press, New York) 240 pp.

Canter, L. W., 1977 *Environmental Impact Assessment* (McGraw-Hill) 331 pp.

Carter, B., 1989 Rising sea level, *Geology Today*, **5(2)**, 63-67.

Carter, D. J. T. and L. Draper, L., 1988, Has the north-east Atlantic become rougher ? *Nature*, **332**, 7 April 1988 p. 494

Carter, R. W. G., 1982, Recent variations in sea-level on the north and east coasts of Ireland and associated shoreline response, *Proc. Royal Irish Academy*, **82B**, 177-187

Carter, R. W. G., 1987 Mans response to sea-level change, In: R. J. W. Devoy, (ed), *op cit*. 464-497.

Carter, R. W. G., 1988 *Coastal Environments*, (Academic Press, London) 617 pp.

Carter, W. E. et al, 1989 *Geodetic Fixing of Tide Gauge Bench Marks*, Report to the IAPSO Commission on Mean Sea level and Tides, Woods Hole Oceanographic Institution, Technical Report CRC-89-5

Cattle, H., 1989 The warming phenomenon, In D. W. Hall and J. C. Doornkamp *op cit*, 15-30

Clark, J. A. and C. S. Lingle, 1977 Future sea level changes due to West Antarctic ice sheet fluctuations, *Nature*, **269**, 206-209

Clark, J. A., Farrel, W. E., and W. R. Peltier, 1978 Global changes in Postglacial sea level: a numerical calculation, *Quaternary Research*, **9**, 265-287

Clark, J. A. and J. A. Primus, 1987 Sea-level changes resulting from future retreat of ice sheets: an effect of $CO_2$ warming of the climate. In: M. J. Tooley and I. Shennan (eds.) *Sea-level Changes*, Institute of British Geographers, Special Publication **20**, 356-370

Clayton, K. M., 1989a, Sediment input from the Norfolk cliffs eastern England - a century of coast protection and its effect, *Jnl. of Coastal Res.*, In Press.

Clayton, K. M., 1989b, Implications of Climatic Change, *Coastal Management*, Institution of Civil Engineers, Thomas Telford

Cooke, R. U., 1987, Geomorphology and environmental management, In: M. J. Clark, K. J. Gregory and A. M. Gurnell (eds.) *Horizons in Physical Geography*, (Macmillan, London) 270-287

Dalrymple, R. A., Biggs, R. B., Dean, R. G., and H. Wang, 1986 Bluff recession rates in Chesapeake Bay, *Jnl. of Waterway Port Coastal and Ocean Eng. (ASCE)*, **112 (1)**, 164-168.

Dean, R. G., 1977 *Equilibrium Beach Profiles*, Technical Report No. 12. (University of Delaware, Newark)

Denness, B., 1984 The greenhouse affair, *Marine Pollution Bulletin*, **15 (10)**, 355-362

Devoy, R. J., 1982 Analysis of the gerological evidence for Holocene sea-level movements in southeast England, *Proc. Geol. Assoc.*, **93 (1)**, 65-90

Devoy, R. J. (ed) 1987 *Sea Surface Studies : A Global View* (Croom Helm)

Eckstein, O., 1958 *Water Resource Development: The Economics of Project Evaluation* (Harvard University Press) 101-160

Emery, K. O. 1980 Relative sea levels from tide-gauge records, *Nat. Acad. Sci. Proc.*, **77**, 6968-6972

Emery, K. O. and D. G. Aubrey, 1985 Glacial rebound and relative sea levels in Europe from tide-gauge records, *Tectonophysics*, **120**, 239-255

Flather, R., 1987 Estiamtes of extreme conditions of tide and surge using a numerical model of the north-west European continental shelf. *Estuarine, Coastal and Shelf Science*, **24**, 69-93

Fleming, C. A. and I. H. Townend, 1989 A coastal management database for East Anglia, *Coastal Zone '89*, In Press.

Forbes, D. L., Taylor, R. B. and J. Shaw, 1989 Shorelines and rising sea levels in eastern Canada, *Episodes*, **12 (1)**, 23-28

Gornitz, V., and S. Lebedeff, 1987, Global sea-level changes during the past century, In: D. Nummedal, O. H. Pilkey, and J. D. Howard (eds), *Sea-level fluctuation and coastal evolution*, SEPM Special Publication, **41**, 3-16

Gretener, P., 1988 Clastic Shorelines - Process to Preservation, *Bulletin of Canadian Petroleum Geology*, **36 (4)**, 413-418.

Gribbin, J., and M. Kelly, 1989 *Winds of Change: Living with the Greenhouse Effect* (Headway, Hodder and Stoughton, London), 162 pp.

Hall, D. W., and J. C. Doornkamp, 1989 *Global Warming: Global Warning* (UNEP-UK Committee, London) 125 pp.

Hansen, J., et al, 1984 *Climatic Processes and Climatic Sensitivity*, Geophysical Monograph, 29, (American Geophysical Union, Washington DC) 130-163

Hansen, J., et al, 1986 The greenhouse effect: projections of global climate change, In J. G. Titus, *Effects of Changes in Stratospheric Ozone and Global Climate*, (United States Environment Protection Agency and UNEP) **Vol 1**, 199-248.

Hansen, J., et al, 1988 Global climate changes as forecast by Goddard Institute for Space Studies three-dimensional model, *J. Geophys. Res.* **93, D8**, 9341-9364.

Harris, R., 1985 Variations in the Durham rainfall and temperature record, 1847-1981. In: M. J. Tooley and G. M. Sheail (eds) *The Climatic Scene*, (George, Allen & Unwin, London), 39-59

Hart, H. C., 1957 Crisis, community, and consent in water politics, *Law and Contemporary Problems*, **XXII**, 510-537

Headworth, H. G., and G. B. Fox, 1986 The South Downs Chalk aquifer: Its development and management, *J. I. W. E. S.*, **40**, 345-361.

Heer, J. E. and D. J. Hagerty, 1977 *Environmental Assessments and Statements* (Van Norstrand Reinhold) 367 pp.

Hewitt, K., and I. Burton, 1971 *The Hazardousness of Place: a Regional Ecology of Damaging Events* (University of Toronto Press, Toronto) 154 pp

Heyworth, A. and C. Kidson, 1982 Sea-level changes in southwest England and Wales, *Proc. Geol. Ass.*, **93 (1)**, 91-111

Hinchcliff, P. R., 1979 *Residual Flows to Estuaries* (Water Planning Unit)

Hoffman, J. S. 1984 Estimates of future sea level rise, In: M. C. Barth and J. G. Titus (eds.) *op cit.*, 79-103

Hoffman, J. S., Keyes, D., and J. G. Titus, 1983 *Projecting Future Sea Level Rise - Methodology, Estimates to the Year 2100 and Research Needs,* US Environmental Protection Agency, Report **EPA 230-09-007.**

Hoffman, J. S., Wells, J. B., and J. G. Titus, 1985 Future global warming and sea level rise, In: Bruun, P. (ed) *Iceland Coastal and River Symposium September 1985, Proceedings,* (National Energy Authority, Reykjavik), pp 53-71, 245-266.

House, J. W. and B Fullerton, 1960 *Teesside at Mid-Century: an Industrial and Economic Survey,* (Macmillan and Co. Ltd., London)

Hulme, M., and P. D. Jones, 1988 *Climatic Change Scenarios for the UK,* Climatic Research Unit Report to Institute of Hydrology, 48 pp.

Hydraulics Research, 1986 *A Macro Review of the Coastline of England and Wales. 1: The North East - St. Abb's Head to the Tees,* Report **No. SR 90,** (Hydraulics Research Ltd., Oxfordshire)

Idso, S. B., 1988 Greenhouse warming of Little Ice Age demise : a critical problem for climatology, *Theoretical Applied Climatology,* **39(1),** 54-56

Intergovernmental Oceanographic Commission, 1990, *The Global Sea-Level Observing System (GLOSS) - Proposed Implementation Plan*

Jardine, W. G., 1982 Sea level changes in Scotland during the last 18,000 years, *Proc. Geol. Ass.,* **93 (1),** 25-41

Jones, T., 1989 Paper presented at the First International Meeting, *Impact of Sea Level Rise on Cities and Regions,* Venice, 11-13 December, 1989.

Karl, T. R., Tarpley, D., Quayle, R. G., Diaz, H. F., Robinson, D. A., and R. S. Bradley, 1989 The recent climate record: what it can and cannot tell us. *Reviews of Geophysics,* **27,** 405-430

Kidson, C. 1982 Sea level changes in the Holocene, *Quaternary Science Reviews,* **1,** 121-151

Knoester, M.,, 1984 Introduction to the Delta case studies. *Water Science Technology*, **16**, 1-9

Lamb, H. H., 1977 *Climate: Present, Past and Future*, **Vol**. 2, *Climatic History and the Future* (Methuen, London) 835 pp.

Lamb, H. H., 1982 *Climate, History and the Modern World* (Methuen, London) 387 pp.

Lamb, H. H., 1988 *Weather, Climate and Human Affairs* (Routledge, London) 364 pp.

Lamb, H. H., and I. Weiss, 1979 On recent changes of the wind and wave regime and the outlook, *Fachl. Mitt. Geophys. BDBW*, **No 194**, Porz-Wahn.

Leatherman, S. P. 1984 Coastal geomorphic responses to sea level rise: Galveston Bay, Texas. In: M. C. Barth and J. G. Titus (eds) *op cit.*, 151-178

Lockwood, J. G. 1979 *Causes of Climate* (Edward Arnold, London) 260 pp.

Marsh, W. M., 1978 *Environmental Analysis for Land Use and Site Planning* (McGraw-Hill)

Meer, J. W. Van der, and K. W. Pilarczyk, 1986 Dynamic stability of breakwaters, rock slopes and gravel beaches, *Proc. ASCE 20th International Conference on Coastal Eng. Taipei.*

Mitchell, J. K., 1974 *Community Response to Coastal Erosion*, Research Paper No. **156** (Department of Geography, University of Chicago) 209 pp.

Mitchell, J. M., 1972 The natural breakdown of the present interglacial and its possible intervention by human activities, *Quaternary Research*, **2(3)**, 436-445

Mitchell, J. M., 1977 The changing climate *Energy and Climate* (Nat. Acad. Sci., Washington) 51-58

Morner, N-A., 1976 Eustasy and geoid changes, *Jl. Geol.*, **84**, 123-151

Nairn, R. B., Pinchin, B. M. and K. L. Philpott, 1986 Cohesive profile development, In: *Cohesive Shores '86*, NRC, Canada, 246-261.

Natural Environment Research Council, 1989a *Our Future World: Global Environmental Research.* Abridged Report to Advisory

Council on Science and Technology, 28 pp.

Natural Environment Research Council, 1989b *Oceans and the Global Carbon Cycle* (Swindon, UK) 17 pp.

Neu, H. J. A., 1984 Inter-annual variations and longer-term changes in the sea state of the North Atlantic from 1970 to 1982, *Jnl. of Geophys. Res,* **89, C4,** 6397-6402.

NRC 1987, *Responding to Changes in Sea Level: Engineering Implications,* (National Academy Press, Washington).

Orford, J., 1987 Coastal Processes: The Coastal Response to sea level variation, In: R. J. N. Devoy *op. cit.,* 415-463.

OTA, 1984 *Wetlands: Their use and regulation,* Office of Technology Assessment, Washington D.C.

Owen, M. W., 1980 *Design of Seawalls Allowing for Wave Overtopping,* Hydraulics Research Report No. **Ex 924.**

Parker, D. J., 1987 The institutional and policy context. In: J. Handmer (ed) *Flood Hazard Management* (Geobooks, Norwich) 35-52

Peck, A. J., and G. B. Allison, 1988 Groundwater and salinity response to climate change, In: *Greenhouse: Planning for Climate Change* (CSIRO, Canberra) 238-251.

Peltier, W. R., and A. M. Tushingham, 1989 Global sea-level rise and the greenhouse effect: might they be connected? *Science,* **244,** 806-810.

Penning-Rowsell, E. C. 1987 Planning and management: physical geography and political processes. In M. J. Clark, K. J. Gregory and A. M. Gurnell (eds.) *Horizons in Physical Geography* (Macmillan, London) 338-352

Philpott, K. L., 1984 Comparison of Cohesive Coasts and Beach Coasts, Coastal Eng. in Canada, Queen's University.

Plass, G. N., 1949 Carbon dioxide and climate, *Scientific American,* **201** (July 1949) 41-47

Pugh, D. T., 1987 *Tides, Surges and Mean Sea-Level* (John Wiley, Chichester) 472 pp.

Pugh, D. T., 1990 Is there a sea level problem? *Proc. Institution of Civil Engineers* (In Press, June 1990)

158

Ratcliff, D., (ed) 1977 *A Nature Conservation Review* Cambridge University Press)

Reed, D. J., 1988 Sediment dynamics and deposition in a retreating coastal marsh, *Estuarine Coastal and Shelf Science,* **26,** 67-79.

Rendel Palmer and Triton, 1977, *Yare Basin Flood Control Study, Vol. 3: River water Quality.*

Rossiter, J. R., 1954 The North Sea storm surge of 31 January and 1 February 1953. *Philosophical Transactions of the Royal Society London,* **A 246,** 371-400

Rossiter, J. R., 1962 Long-term variations in sea level, In: N. M. Hill (ed) *The Sea 1* (Interscience Publishers, London) 590-610

Rye, H., 1976 Long-term changes in the North Sea wave climate and their importance for extreme wave predictions, *Marine Science Communications,* **2 (6),** 419-448.

Ryecroft, M. J. 1982 Analysing atmospheric carbon dioxide levels, *Nature,* **295,** 190-191

Seidels, S. and D. Keyes, 1983 *Can We Delay a Greenhouse Warming?* (Government Printing Office, Washington, DC.)

Sewell, W. R. D., 1964 Benefit-cost analysis and the evaluation of alternative adjustments to floods, In: *Spatial Organisation of Land* (Oregon State University Press, Corvallis, Oregon)

Sewell, W. R. D., 1965 *Water management and floods in the Fraser River Basin,* Research Paper No. **100** (Department of Geography, University of Chicago) 163 pp.

Shennan I., 1983 Flandrian and late Devensian sea level changes and crustal movements in England and Wales, In: D. E. Smith and A. G. Dawson (eds.) *Shorelines and Isostasy,* (Academic Press, London), 255-283

Shennan, I., 1987a Impacts on the Wash of sea-level rise, In: P. Doody and B. Barnett (eds) *The Wash and its Environment,* Research and Survey in Nature Conservation No. 7, (Nature Conservancy Council, Peternorough) 77-90

Shennan, I., 1987b, Holocene sea-level changes in the North Sea, In: M. J. Tooley and I. Shennan (eds) *Sea-Level Changes* (Blackwell, Oxford) 109-151

*Bibliography and references*

Shennan, I., 1989a Holocene crustal movements and sea-level changes in Great Britain. *Jl. of Quaternary Science,* **4**, 77-89

Shennan, I., 1989b, Holocene sea-level changes and crustal movements in the North Sea region: an experiment with regional eustasy. In D. B. Scott, P. A. Pirazzoli and C. A. Honig (eds.) *Late Quaternary Sea-level Correlation and Applications,* NATO ASI Series **C25**, (Kluwer Academic Publishers, Dordrecht) 1-25

Shennan, I., and M. J. Tooley, 1987 Conspectus of fundamental and strategic research on sea-level changes, In: M. J. Tooley and I. Shennan (eds.) *Sea Level Changes,* ( Blackwell), 371-390

Sproxton, I., 1989 The impact of projected sea-level rise on wildlife habitats of the Tees estuary. *Newsletter of the Cleveland Wildlife Trust* **30**, 12-14

Stewart, R. W. 1989 Sea level rise or coastal subsidence? *Atmosphere-Ocean* **27**, 461-477

Thompson, G., Law, F. M., 1983 An assessment of the fluvial tidal flooding problem of the River Ancholme, UK. *Proc. I.V.G.G. Symposium on Assessment of Natural Hazards,* Hamburg.

Titus, J. G., 1986 Greenhouse effect, sea level rise and coastal zone management, *Coastal Zone Management Journal,* **14 (3)**, 147-171.

Titus, J. G., 1987 The Greenhouse effect, rising sea level and society's response, In: R. J. N. Devoy (ed.) *op cit.* 499-528.

Titus J. G., and M. C. Barth, 1984 An overview of causes and ef ects of sea level rise, In: M. C. Barth and J. G. Titus (eds.) *op cit.*

Tooley, M. J. 1978 The history of Hartlepool Bay. *International Jl. of Nautical Archaeology and Underwater Exploration,* **7**, 71-75

Tooley, M. J., 1982 Sea level changes in northern England, *Proc. Geol. Ass.,* **93 (1)**, 43-51

Tooley, M. J. 1989 Floodwaters mark sudden rise. *Nature,* **342**, 20-21

Townend, I. H., 1986, Coastal studies to establish suitable coastal management procedures, *Jnl. of Shoreline Management,* **2**, 131-154.

Townend, I. H., and P. McLaren, 1989 *Anglian Coastal Management Atlas,* Sir William Halcrow & Partners Ltd.

Van Der Veen, C. J. 1989 Projecting future sea level, *Survey in Geophysics,* **9 (3-4),** 389-418

Vellinga, P., 1984 A tentative description of a universal erosion profile for sandy beaches and rock beaches, *Coastal Eng.,* **8,** 171-188.

Wakelin, M. J., 1989 The deterioration of a coastline, *Coastal Management,* Institution of Civil Engineers, Thomas Telford.

Warrick, R. A., and T. L. M. Wigley (eds) (In Press) *International workshop on climate change, sea level, severe tropical storms and associated impacts (Norwich, UK, 1-4 September, 1987)*

Warrick, R., Wilkinson, A., and T. M. L. Wigley, 1989 *Estimating global-mean sea level change, 1982-2050,* Unpublished progress report, Climatic Research Unit, University of East Anglia, March 1989.

White, G. F. and J. E. Haas, 1975 *Assessment of Research on Natural Hazards* (MII Press, Cambridge, Mass.) 487 pp.

Whittow, J., 1987 Natural hazards - adjustments and mitigation. In: M. J. Clark, K. J. Gregory and A. M. Gurnell (eds.) *Horizons in Physical Geography* (Macmillan, London) 307-321

Wiin-Nielsen, A. C. 1989 The greenhouse effect : A review of data and model studies; Summaries of presentations; First International Meeting, Impact of Sea Level Rise on Cities and Regions, Venice. 7-13

Wilson, J. A., 1985 The influence of an artificial hydraulic regime on water quality in the tidal River Lagan, Northern Ireland, *J. I. W. E. S.* **39,** 423-436

Wigley T. M., 1989 Paper presented at Annual Meeting of Impacts of sea-level rise project, Cork, September 1989

Wood, F. B. 1988 On the need for the validation of the temperature trends with respect to urban warming. *Climatic Change,* **12** , 297-312

*Bibliography and references*

Woodworth, P. L., 1987 Trends in UK mean sea level, *Marine Geodesy*, **11**, 57-87.

# THE GREENHOUSE EFFECT AND RISING SEA LEVELS
## A PROGRAMME OF ACTION

### AT NATIONAL LEVEL

1. Establish a team to evaluate the continuing research into the greenhouse effect, and to assess the implications for changes in sea level, especially as they will affect the UK.

2. Establish a uniform technique for the local assessment of the reality of changing sea levels.

3. Carry out a comprehensive programme to evaluate the areas most at risk, their current occupancy, and the value of the stock at risk.

4. Provide planning guidelines for areas at risk.

5. Provide the means of integrating national and local action.

6. Re-assess the policy concerning coastal defences which remain a central government responsibility.

7. Prepare and disseminate information on the alternative strategies available at local government level.

8. Evaluate the present system for providing storm warnings, and if necessary introduce improvements which are continually up-graded as technology improves.

9. Assess the feasibility of providing a national insurance scheme in relation to damage in coastal areas.

10. Maintain a programme of communication, discussion and debate between national authorities and local authorities, and between both of these and political groups.

## AT LOCAL LEVEL

1. Establish a team to monitor future forecasts of changing sea levels.

2. Commission an Environmental Impact Assessment specifically for the area under the authority's administration.

3. Establish and maintain local monitoring stations.

4. Either through 2. above or separately, establish the sites and areas most at risk.

5. Establish a local policy for coping with changes in sea level and other secondary effects of climatic change.

6. Establish a local programme for the dissemination of information.

7. Maintain an integrated approach with neighbouring, regional and national authorities.

*Action list devised by Dr. J. C. Doornkamp. Approval of this list by MAFF (or any other authority) is neither implied nor intended.*

*Readers are also referred to the House of Lords Select Committtee on Science and Technology Report on the Greenhouse Effect.*

**"THERE IS HOPE FOR A SAFER ENVIRONMENT, BUT
IT CANNOT BE ACHIEVED EASILY OR SOON."**

Burton et al (1978) p 223